ARROWORDS

ARROWORDS

MORE THAN 250 PUZZLES

This edition published in 2022 by Arcturus Publishing Limited
26/27 Bickels Yard, 151–153 Bermondsey Street,
London SE1 3HA

AD010806UK

Printed in the UK

1

Dome-shaped dessert		Game played on horseback	Use again after processing		Part of a ship's cargo thrown overboard		Attorney
b	o	m	b	e	Geological period of time	e	r	a
Ms Parton, songstress	l	Crippled	Popular pet	t	a	t	Special way of doing something
d	o	l	l	y	Where the sun shines and the stars twinkle!	s	k	y
Condiment made of fruit and sugar	Upward movement	a	Large wading bird	c	r	a	n	e
j	a	m	Change direction	l	Mark or flaw	m	a	r
Number considered lucky	s	e	v	e	n	Cut of meat	c	Country that borders France
Sales slip	r	Bludgeon	l	Mosque official	Narrow runner used for gliding over snow	s	k	i
r	e	c	e			t	Draw	t
Standard	n	o	r	m	Hour at which something is due (inits)	t	t	a
	t	s	Be of service	a	v	a	i	l
Of a thing	Gammon	h	a	m	Metal device used in a lock	k	e	y

2

Acacia secretion used as a thickener (3,6)	▼	Smoke-stack of a ship / Adult male	▼	Temperature scale	▼	Lack of colour / Stand with two legs	▼	Clothes drier / Printer's mark
G	U	M	A	R	A	B	I	C
Granny / Owner of a hostelry	n	a	h	Former money unit in Italy / Ova	l	i	t	a
I	N	N	K	E	E	P	E	R
Made a loud, deep ringing sound	e	Disregard / Assumed name	i	g	n	o	r	e
C	L	A	N	G	E	D	Not as rich	t
Garland	Fewer / Fill with high spirits	l	e	s	s	Capital of Tibet	P	Spanish boy's name
L	e	l	Informal conversation	Pigswill / Flow back	3	L	O	P
Fabric / Surface to scrub clothes on	a	▼	▼	Garden tool / Available	h	o	e	▼
W	a	s	h	b	o	a	r	d
▼	t	Malt beer	a b	b	v	s	e	ri
H	e	a	t	Herb of the Pacific islands with an edible root	t	a	r	o

3

Fuel derived from petroleum	P	Relaxation	b	Chances	▼	Spinning toys / Old weight measure	▼	Cardinal number
N	A	R	D	R	O	B	E	Native American tent
Clothes closet / Crimson	R	E	D	Type of boat / Long fishes	P	N	N	T
Appraise	A	S	S	E	S	S	Roman love poet, born in 43 BC	E
A	F	T	Enfold	E	Jump on one foot	H	O	P
Toward the stern of a ship	F	Arm covering	S	L	E	E	V	E
H	I	G	H	S	Untruth	L	I	E
___ and lows	N	Native of Edinburgh, for example	e	Collective noun for whales	G	Calamitous	D	Persistently scolds
Enclosed conduit for a fluid	Dish of cold vegetables / Spend	S	a	L	A	D	US government unit (inits)	N
d	u	C	E	Aluminium silicate mineral	M	I	C	A
London district / Festival	S	O	h	O	Equip	R	I	G
f	e	t	e	Small green vegetables	P	E	A	S

Suffering delusions of persecution	p	Sturdy upright pole	d	Excavates	▼	Influence unfairly / Attack	0	Globe
e	a	m	i	l	n	a	R	Abnormally fat
Usual / Boisterous practical joke	r	a	y	Yob deterrent (inits) / Pitcher	A	s	b	0
Appraise	A	S	S	e	S	S	Secret look	b
a	m	t	Place out of sight	w	Chimpanzee, for example	u	p	l
Insect	l	Similar things placed in order	s	e	r	i	e	s
a	r	r	e	r	Side sheltered from the wind	l	e	e
Clothes drier	d	Nipple	c	Artificial covering for a tooth	C	Filled tortilla	r	Naked
Affectedly dainty or refined	Behave towards / Which person?	t	r	u	n	N	Equality	n
t	w	e	e	Daddy	p	a	p	A
Detest / Doves' home	h	a	t	e	Automobile	c	a	r
c	o	t	e	Diameter of a tube or gun barrel	b	0	R	e

8

5

Reverie / Clothes closet	d	Quantity of paper	d	Biblical first man	p	Game on horseback / Brigand	n	___ Kelly, famous Australian bush-ranger
W	A	R	D	R	O	B	E	Arabian country
Old-fashioned affirmative answer	y	e	a	Noble-woman / Glasgow native, eg	L	a	d	y
Small purple plum	d	a	m	s	o	n	Bitter	e
a	r	m	Capital of Arizona	C	Barrier that contains the flow of water	d	a	m
Branch	e	Law force	P	O	L	I	C	Z
y	a	c	h	t	Malleable metallic element that resists corrosion	t	i	n
Racing vessel	m	Scottish hillside	o	Fluid used for writing	I	Leak through	d	Compact mass (of earth)
Ripped	Great feast / Globe	B	e	a	n	o	In what way?	I
t	o	r	n	Cosmetic used to darken the edges of the eyes	K	O	h	a
Attack / Mountain goat	r	a	i	d	Facility exhibiting wild animals	Z	O	O
l	B	E	X	Exhibiting lustful desires	l	e	w	d

Hypothetical remedy for all ills (4-3)	b	Incinerate	Infrequent	R	Hang around	A	Charitable gifts	Diminutive of Henry
C	U	R	E	A	L	L	Asked	A
Cosmic	r	Charged particle	Ballroom dance	R	U	M	B	A
U	n	i	V	E	R	S	A	L
Residence of a clergyman	Love affair	Male child of a spouse and former partner	Fruiting spike of a cereal plant	Expression of surprise or mild alarm	K	Snake-like fish	d	Baby goat
M	A	N	S	E	e	e		K
Climbing plant supporter	m	Narration	t	a	i	e	Prongs of a fork	l
b	o	w	e	r	Abbreviation seen after a company's name	L	T	D
Coloured part of the eye	U	Hostel	p	Garment that covers the head and face	V	A person in general	l	Division of a tennis match
i	r	i	s	Long periods of time	e	o	n	s
Capital of West Germany from 1949 to 1989	Candidate	n	o	m	i	n	e	e
b	e	r	n	In case	L	e	s	t

7

Insect between larva and adult stage	▼ P	Repeated pro-gramme	Forceful	▼	Minute life form	Embrace	▼	Complain
Official literary language of Pakistan	► U	R	▼ D	U	Stocky short-legged harness horse	▼		
Frame-work that supports climbing plants	► P							Small child
▼	A		Tendency to seek distraction or relief from reality		Social insect	► A	N	▼ T
Airborne soldier (abbr)	Con-sumers	►		▼			Augment	I
►					Animal kept for com-panionship	►	▼ A	d
Takes short quick breaths	Hoarfrost	Water frozen in the solid state	►			Sailing vessel	d	Romany
►	▼				Barrel	► t	d	▼ G
Heather		Added to	Food wrapped in a pastry shell	►		a	Took in solid food	y
Country, capital Bamako	►	▼			Faucet	► C	▼ V	P
►			Religious orders	►		H		s
Chaps	Badly lit	►			Interjection used as a greeting	► t		y

11

8

Turn into / Express a good opinion of	▼	Of sound	▼	Aluminium silicate mineral	▼	Unit of electric current (abbr)	▼	Deer horn
▼				▼				
Acute abdominal pain		Small drink ►				Fleshy cover of some seeds		Entreaty
▼				High mountain / Mother of Zeus	▼			▼
Round vegetable	Study area in a library / Corrupt practice ►			▼				
▼		▼	Have a lofty goal	Rent / Cup without a handle ►				
Sickness	Tall tower referred to in the Bible ►		▼				Direct one's attention on something	
▼						Having started life	▼	Town in south-western England
Leader of an Arab village	Health resort / Quality of a colour ►				Baby's napkin	▼		▼
▼	▼				Repro-ductive cells ►			
Conduit for carrying off waste products		Remorse ►						
▼				To the ___ degree (to the utmost) ►				

Impossible to correct or redress	▼	Yelp	▼	Third son of Adam and Eve	▼	Wise Men who brought gifts to Jesus	▼
Cereal crop ►	▼			Cain's brother ►		Use a dragnet	Archaic term for army
Renegade ►				English flower, also a girl's name			Elegant water-birds
⚑				▼			▼
Inflammation of the kidneys	Forbid	Distance across		Propel with oars ►			
Flows back ►	▼	▼		Mother of the ancient Irish gods ►			
Act presumptuously ►				In a state of uncertainty, perplexed (2,3)		Boys, men	
⚑			Voluntary contributions to aid the poor ►	▼		▼	
Grape plant	Towards the rear ►				Little rascal		Lyrical poem
Unsound ►			Cylindrical store-tower ►		▼		▼
Network structure	Provided with a particular motif ►						
⚑				Recess in a church ►			

13

Clair-voyance (inits)		Overly diluted		Concise and full of meaning	Fabric for a painting		Part of the lower jaw	Rigid piece of metal
Change							Strongly motivated to succeed	
			Opera by Verdi					
Expec-torated	Diluting agent							
				Enclosed		Smoky smelly atmos-phere		Fixed
Australian term for a young kangaroo	Reminds, prompts		Coffee shops					
Centre of attention								
Top or highest point of a thing		Went on horseback	Weedy annual grass		Local time at the 0 meridian (inits)			
						Flurry		Append
Rise upward into the air					Mother of the ancient Irish gods			
Haemor-rhage	Feared							
					Not divisible by two			

11

Internal organs collectively	▼	Allude to	Common amphibian	▼	Infrequent	▼	Foun-dation	Crystalline rock that can be cut for jewellery
◣					▼		Carry	
Fast narrow current in the air (3,6)		A couple	Fritter away	►		▼		
◣		▼						
Ambit	Thin pancake		Associate who works with others	Consci-ousness of one's own identity		Plot of ground in which plants grow		Acquire
◣	▼		▼		Implore	►		▼
Electric under-ground railway		Fever	►				Flexible twig of a willow	
◣				One of the two symbols used in Morse	►		▼	
Intend to express or convey		___ Baba		Ancient Semitic deity	▼	Enclosure for swine		Charge
◣		▼		Expression of incredulity (2,2)	►		▼	▼
Arabian ruler	Beneficiary of a will	►						
◣			Ancient Greek harp	►				

15

12

Chinese communist leader (1893–1976)		Melt		Cider fruit	Proportions		Collapsible shelter	Hideout
Have a lofty goal							Banter	
				Gambling stake				
Cage	Make level							
				Predatory freshwater fish, with a long body	Musical passage in quicker time			Issue of a magazine
Deaden (a sound or noise)	Army division		Temporary police force					
Not included on a register								
Christmas pie filling		Indian bread, baked in a clay oven	Cheats, swindles		Repast		Four-wheeled motor vehicle	
Ultimate principle of the universe				Case for needles				
Organs of locomotion and balance in fishes	Yellowish-red dye used to colour fabric							
				Silly or foolish person (coll)				

13

Alliance begun in 1949 (inits)	▼	West Indian dance	▼	Double-reed woodwind instrument	▼	Conspi-cuously and offensively loud	▼	Covering that protects an inside surface
The food of the gods ►	▼							
Ultimate principle of the universe ►				Chore		Lesser		Floral leaf
►				▼		▼		▼
Occa-sionally	Auction item		Burning ►				Highly incendiary liquid used in fire bombs	
Relax	▼							
Corrode, as with acid		American raccoon	Basic unit of money in Iceland ►				▼	
⌐		▼	Examina-tion con-ducted by word of mouth ►					
Winning all the tricks in bridge (5,4)	Crimson		Female member of a religious order	Expire	Cover with insulation to prevent heat loss			Encoun-tered
⌐	▼		▼	▼	▼			▼
Case for needles ►				Alcoholic brew ►				
Have supper ►				Local time at the 0 meridian (inits) ►				

Not easily explained	▼	Lacking in pigment	▼	Produce offspring	▼	Any leafy plants eaten as vegetables	▼	Sea vessel
Place in which photographs are developed	▼							
▶				Small drink		Wide open		Abodes
At rest	At a lower place ▶			▼		▼		▼
Beating ▶							Oil extracted from the flax plant	
Proclaim	Capable of being done with the means at hand		Religious song ▶				▼	
▶	▼		▼	In what place?	Food wrapped in a pastry shell ▶			
Dog ___, tattered	Drizzle			Female birds ▶				
▶		▼			Chimpan-zee, for example	Side sheltered from the wind		Engage in espionage
Exclude ▶				Beers ▶	▼	▼		▼
Untruth / To the full extent (poetically) ▶				Quick look ▶				
▶			Of poor stature ▶					

15

Machine tool	▼	Maker	Bath powder	▼	Useless or tedious printed material	Windpipe	▼	Cure
Carry out in practice ▶		▼	▼			▼		Tidings
Cable-car ▶					Dashed ▶			▼
Assist ▶					Alcoholic brew ▶			
⚑					Cause to be bored		Large vase	
Area of sand sloping down to the water	Spicy tomato sauce		Circuits of a race-course	In the way indicated ▶	▼		▼	
Fighter ▶	▼		▼					Anxious
⚑				Harangue ▶				▼
Airborne soldier		Little insect		Evil-looking old woman		Item of equipment used in baseball	Expend	
Girdle ▶		▼		▼	Bread roll ▶	▼	▼	
⚑			Collect or gather, hoard ▶					
Admirer	Pull sharply	▶			Golfing device ▶			

19

16

Potato (coll)		Conduct work	Which person? ——— About (2,2)		Fully extended, especially in length		Straighten out	
Winnie-the-___, A A Milne's bear					Employ			
Displace							Musical study	
				Sketchy summary of the main points	Division of a tennis match			
"Beware the ___ of March", saying	Ornament made of ribbon, given as an award							
Waited on	Audition (3,3)		Enter-prising or ambitious drive		Hasten			
								Baby's wear
US city known for casinos and easy divorce					Cardinal number			
Divisions of a day		Heroic					Belonging to you and me	
					Jump lightly			
Corset		Forfeit (4,2)						
					Lacking moisture			

Line up | Sword lily | | ___ Cup, golf tournament | | Suddenly and unexpectedly | | Release (3,2) / ___ Baba |

Scottish form of the word 'no'

Fritter away | Everything | | Traded / Large cask or barrel

Synthetic hairpiece / Title of a baronet

Pastry case | | ___ Major, constellation / Fix, settle | | | | | Enquire

Brother of George Gershwin / Felines | | | | Peaceful

Coconut meat | Large body of water | Green salad vegetable / Harangue

Travel on the piste / Irritation

American raccoon / Bring back | | | | | | Wing of an insect | Treat skins to convert them into leather

Insect / Explosive compound (inits) | | | Kin group

Intonate

21

18

Gelling agent	▼	Cambodian monetary units	▼	Fruit preserves	▼	Hand tool for boring holes	▼	Underground tunnels
Composed of relatively large particles ►	▼							
Intention ►				Caps, berets, etc		Not in any way		Stinking
►				▼				▼
Air-___, product used for purifying a room ►	Narrow runner used for gliding over snow		Got up ►					
►	▼					Part of an animal	Cinnamon-yielding tree	
Thing of value		Not diluted	Ancestry, bloodline ►			▼	▼	
►		▼		Departed ►				
Stick to firmly	Evil		Man's title	Stretch		Day before a festival		volatile, smelling salts
Unwarranted, without foundation ►	▼		▼	▼		▼		▼
►						By way of ►		
Method of producing designs on cloth		Disclose ►						

Indonesian island	▼	Dwells or waits	▼	Manage, make do	▼	Disease marked by intense headache and fever	▼	Projecting edge of a roof
Higher than average (5,3) ►	▼							
Rim ►				Placed in position		Fool, twit (coll)		Daniel ___, English novelist
▶				▼				▼
Placed into an inferior position	Shortened forename of US president Lincoln		Liquorice-flavoured seeds ►					
Designate ►	▼						Feel sorrow	
Skilful in physical move-ments		Plant life	Australian wild dog ►				▼	
▶	▼			Covering for a wheel ►				
Member of a body of church singers	Pelvic joint		Having the surface exposed and painful	Tavern		Number indicated by the Roman X		Soften by soaking in water
▶	▼		▼	▼		▼		▼
Islamic republic formerly called Persia ►					The night before ►			
Chess piece ►					Mesh ►			

Preside over (a meeting)	Podium	⬛◤ ▼	Salt water	⬛◤ ▼	Locate exactly	⬛◤ ▼	Large artery / Very small	⬛◤ ▼
⬛◣					___ Jima, Japanese island ⬛◤		▼	
Fire-raising	Cereal crop		Closer to the centre ⬛◤ / Select					
⬛◣	▼		▼		Caress gently / Travel over snow			
Thaw		Mexican monetary unit ⬛◤ / Theft				▼	Musical composition for two performers	
⬛◣		▼		Child / Des-patched ⬛◤				Emphasis
___ blanche, full discretionary power	Jelly based on fish or meat stock		Air cavity in the skull ⬛◤ / Short, sharp nail	▼				▼
⬛◣	▼		▼	Small measure of drink ⬛◤ / Record				
Of limited quantity ⬛◤ / Elaborate display					▼	Sealed metal storage container	Hallucinogenic drug (inits)	
⬛◣						▼	▼	
Fluid ejected by cuttlefish ⬛◤ / Frosty			Exceed ⬛◤					
⬛◣			Curves, meanders ⬛◤					

24

21

Club	▼	Burrowing animal	▼	Acquiesce	▼	Region bordering Israel and Egypt	Mental deterioration	▼
Open to debate	►	▼						
►				Periodically repeated sequence		Edict with force of law in tsarist Russia	Form of address	
Celebrity	Due to, on account of	►		▼		▼	▼	
►					Family	►		
Church associated with a convent	Personification of a familiar idea		Graph	►				
►	▼		Tubes		Add together		Salvers	
___ King Cole, jazz pianist and singer		Former Spanish monetary unit	►	▼		▼	▼	
►				High mountain		For each		Observe
Wise Men who brought gifts to Jesus		Argentine plain	►	▼		▼		▼
►					Calm central region of a cyclone	►		
Biblical tower intended to reach to heaven		Not dense	►					

25

Dull pain	Native tribe of Canada and North America	Cuts into two equal pieces	▼	Harmless tropical house-lizard	Excellent	Confused scuffle	▼	Motor car
⌐	▼	▼		Com-placent	▶			
Tennis 'bat' ▶								Ox from Tibet
Northern deer with very large antlers ▶				Cunning man-oeuvre	▶			▼
⌐							Long and distinct period of history ▼	
Aficionado	Positive declaration		Walk unsteadily	If not, then	⌐		▼	
⌐	▼		▼	▼	Offensively un-pleasant odour	Jarring		Slabs of grass and grass roots ▼
Coat in fat	Passé (3,3)	▶				▼		
⌐					Fireside mat		Cereal grass	
Footwear that covers the lower legs	Great fear ▶			▼		▼		
⌐				Branch of the American armed services ▶				
Lean-fleshed fish similar to cod	Rectifies, redresses ▶							

23

Far from the intended target	▼	Second person pronoun	▼	Picture painted on a plaster wall	Russian prison camp for political prisoners	▼	Cap made of soft cloth	▼
Port on the east coast of Sicily ►	▼							
Foot digit ――― Hinder or prevent ►				Government tax on imports or exports	Mats		Objective case of 'thou'	
◣				▼	▼		▼	
Bionic man or woman		Captured ――― Most direct route ►						
◣		▼				Heavy, sullen		Blood-sucking African fly
Bundle (of straw, for example)	Equine animal		Small area of land ――― British snake ►			▼		▼
◣	▼		▼		High-flying singing bird		Morass	
Former sweetheart (3,5) ――― Very dry ►						▼	▼	
◣				Entrance passage into a mine ►				
Scoffers ――― Ale ►								
◣				Leg joint ►				

Small slender gull with a forked tail	Blyton, author	Failing in what duty requires	▼	Finely powdered tobacco	Modified leaf of a plant	Edible seaweed	▼	Land-locked republic in Western Africa
◢				Deceive through coaxing or wheedling				
Having no personal preference								Dull
UN banking/finance agency (inits)				Eager				
◢						Promissory note (inits)		
Large and complex construction	Lucky charm		Sea-girt territory	Drunkards				
◢					Pare	Dormant		Chemical element such as iron or chromium
Desert garden	Metallic element, symbol Na							
◢					Partly goat, the god of woods and fields		US government unit (inits)	
Constructed	Characteristic to be considered							
◢				Vocal music				
Introduce to solid food	Of teeth							

Pouches	Child of Adam and Eve	Decanter	▼	Literary com-position	Greased	Not a single person (2-3)	▼	Holy women
▼	▼	▼		Burden of respon-sibility	▼	▼		
Citadel ▶								Small child
Geological period of time ▶				Bewil-dered				▼
▶						Auto-mated computer program		
Portable enclosure in which a baby can be left	Peruser of text		Plantation	Devices which fit locks ▶			▼	
▶	▼		▼	▼	Financial obligation	Love intensely		Occur-rence
Brook	Dignified and sombre in manner ▶					▼		▼
▶					Fruit of a rose plant		Legendary bird	
Exces-sively quick		On land ▶			▼		▼	
▶				Golf club with a narrow metal head ▶				
Vegetable matter used as a fuel		Await ▶						

Secreting organ in animals	Establish-ments where alcohol is served	▼	Au revoir	▼	Acting game, popular at Christmas	▼	Acute pain ___ Khan	▼
					Evil-looking old woman ►		▼	
Temporary police force	Egg cells		Adult insect ___ Enclosure for swine ►					
►	▼		▼		Dashed ___ Exclama-tion of disgust ►			
Netlike	Brass instrument ___ Lucidity ►				▼		Hard durable wood	
►	▼		Bustle ___ Des-patched ►				▼	Showy dress or decoration
Digging implement	Elf or fairy		Bundle of straw ___ Crash out ►	▼				▼
►	▼		▼	Glide over snow ___ Fictional creature ►				
Criticism disguised as praise ___ Being ►				▼		Mesh	Animal kept as a domestic pet	
►					▼	▼		
Of a thing ► ___ Slightly insane			Eye secretion ►					
►			Short simple song ►					

27

Poly-nesian rain dance / Clear		Body	Weird / Creep towards, slowly		News media, generally (6,6)		Point in orbit	
					Retired person (inits)			
Four-wheel covered carriage							Dodge	
				In a foreign country	Shortened version of a man's name			
Boy's name	Laugh quietly or with restraint							
Dim-inished	Former monetary unit of Portugal		Seven people con-sidered as a unit		Gradation of a colour			
								In what place?
Prophet					Stitch together			
Flat-topped hill		Excla-mation					Turkish title of respect	
					Shortened forename of US president Lincoln			
Caprine animals		Celebra-tion of Christ's resur-rection						
					Organ of sight			

Castrated bull	▼	Long deposit of beach material (4,3)	Encourage	▼	Closer to the centre	Family who ruled Florence in the 15th century	▼	Collection of objects laid on top of each other
Huge destructive wave ▶		▼	▼			▼		Newly made
Take home ▶					Fairy ▶			▼
Give rise to ▶								
▶					Immediate		Conceited, self-centred person ▼	
Arrange	Prickly desert plants		Crescent-shaped yellow fruit	Decorates with frosting ▶	▼		▼	
Train driver's compartment ▶	▼		▼	Close by, near ▶				
▶						Region		Satisfy completely
Annoy continually		Ailing		Makes lacework by knotting or looping ▶		▼		▼
Popular coffee-flavoured liqueur (3,5) ▶		▼						
▶			Structure in which animals lay eggs ▶					
Oven for firing pottery	Produce milk for a baby to drink ▶							

More alien	Tertiary	Edge	▼	Having negative qualities	Receive an academic degree	Formal expression of praise	▼	Coloured part of the eye
⌐	▼	▼			▼	▼		Situation certain to end in failure (2-3)
Concealed ▶				Destroy completely ▶				▼
▶			Draw back	Too ▶				
Aspire		Make new ▶	▼				Tennis stroke	
▶				Fruit, a tangerine and grapefruit cross ▶			▼	
Inactive	Saturate	Wax drawing implement ▶						
Foundation of a carriage-way for vehicles	▼	Zealous		Broken husks of the seeds of cereal grains		Information		Measure of land
⌐		▼				▼	Paddle	▼
Declare ▶				Continuous portion of a circle ▶			▼	
▶			Lady Nancy ___, first woman MP ▶					
Travel on the piste	Com-motion ▶			Profound emotion inspired by a deity ▶				

30

Breathes noisily, as if exhausted ▼		Tutored, trained	Bullets, etc (abbr)	▼	Dexterous	Inflict a severe defeat on (slang)	▼	Printed characters
Learned institution ►	▼	▼			▼			Tempest
A few ►				Increases ►			▼	
Brochure ►								
⚑				Loss by use or natural decay		Morally strict		
Berkshire town, famous for its racecourse	Send (payment)		Spanish rice dish	Don ►	▼		▼	
Fabric with prominent rounded crosswise ribs ►	▼		▼	Cuckoo pint, for example ►				
⚑						Particle		Biblical garden
Awards for winning		Resin-like substance secreted by certain insects		London art gallery ►		▼		▼
Unlucky (3-5) ►		▼						
⚑				Coagulated blood from a wound ►				
Latin phrase: 'and elsewhere' (2,2)	Troglodytes	►						

31

<table>
<tr><td>Change to ice
———
Small restaurant</td><td>▼</td><td>Enquired
———
Affray, fracas</td><td>▼</td><td>Michigan's Motor City</td><td>▼</td><td>Colossus
———
Harnesses</td><td>▼</td><td>Fungus that infects cereal plants</td></tr>
<tr><td>◣</td><td>▼</td><td></td><td></td><td></td><td></td><td>▼</td><td></td><td>▼</td></tr>
<tr><td>Large deer ▶
———
Putting off</td><td></td><td></td><td></td><td>Pull apart ▶</td><td></td><td></td><td></td><td></td></tr>
<tr><td>◣</td><td></td><td></td><td></td><td></td><td></td><td></td><td></td><td></td></tr>
<tr><td>Last letter of the alphabet ▶
———
For each</td><td></td><td></td><td></td><td>Aware of ▶
———
Features</td><td></td><td></td><td></td><td></td></tr>
<tr><td>◣</td><td></td><td>Belonging to him ▶
———
Aquatic creature</td><td>▼</td><td></td><td></td><td></td><td>Circles of light around saints' heads</td><td></td></tr>
<tr><td>Takes part in an informal con-versation ▶</td><td>Cover
———
Large crowd of people ▶</td><td></td><td>▼</td><td></td><td></td><td>Bohemian dance</td><td>▼</td><td>Not a single person (2-3)</td></tr>
<tr><td>◣</td><td>▼</td><td></td><td></td><td></td><td>Greek deity, half man, half goat</td><td>▼</td><td></td><td>▼</td></tr>
<tr><td>Excessive (inits) ▶
———
Projecting window</td><td></td><td></td><td></td><td>Game on horseback ▶
———
Caustic solution</td><td></td><td></td><td></td><td></td></tr>
<tr><td>◣</td><td></td><td></td><td></td><td>▼</td><td>Toilet (coll) ▶</td><td></td><td></td><td></td></tr>
<tr><td>Small boat ▶
———
Low-lying wetland</td><td></td><td></td><td></td><td></td><td>Range of knowledge ▶</td><td></td><td></td><td></td></tr>
<tr><td>◣</td><td></td><td></td><td>Rub out ▶</td><td></td><td></td><td></td><td></td><td></td></tr>
</table>

Fusilli, for example		Axle	Male sovereign		Adipose	Person who dusts, vacuums, etc		Successor
With a side or oblique glance								Panel forming the lower part of a wall
Eject fluid from the mouth					Cover			
Dye with a colour					Epoch, age			
					Musical instrument		Have a go	
Shabby, seedy	Fight (3,2)		Variety of agate	Aware of				
Drool								Woody part of plants
				African antelope with long straight horns				
Eager		Burned remains	___ and buts, objections		___ Khan	Pull		
Cab					Com-pletely			
			Musical form con-sisting of a repeated theme					
Call for help (inits)	Features				Yearly assembly of share-holders (inits)			

Cause to be alert and energetic	▼	Painful eyelid swellings	▼	Deep yellow colour	Gait	▼	Supreme god of ancient Greek mythology	▼ ▼
⌞								
Informal term for all the world's oceans (5,4)		Calf meat		Of a quantity that can be counted	Fungus producing black spores		Change	
		▼		▼	▼		▼	
Plasma ▶						Banqueted		Whole number
Cotton fabric with a short pile	Dodge		Civilian clothing ▶			▼		▼
⌞	▼							
Ice cream dishes served with a topping		Hen-pecks	Twofold		Mr Garfunkel, singer-songwriter ▶			
⌞		▼	▼				Be in debt	
Coat with plaster ▶					Duvet warmth rating ▶		▼	
▶					Lamb's mother ▶			
Founded upon law	Slim ▶							

Express or state clearly	Subtle difference in meaning	Large pots for making tea	▼	Army division	▼	Female operatic star	▼	Alternative
⌐	▼	▼						
Swiss canton ▶				Ms Braun, Hitler's mistress		Mark (~) placed over the letter 'n' in Spanish		Assigned a rank
Spiny insectivore with a long tongue ▶				▼		▼		▼
⌐			Spectacles		Lyricist, ___ Gershwin			
Measures used in printing ⌐		Bile, the fluid secreted by the liver	▼				Ailing	
⌐				Edgar Allan ___, author	Directly or exactly, straight ▶		▼	
Inform	Variety of agate	Add on, supplement ▶		▼				
⌐	▼				Breath or spirit in Chinese philosophy	Perennial herb with grey-green bitter leaves		Small amount
Upper body		Clandestine ▶			▼			▼
⌐				Polynesian rain dance ▶				
___ Maclachlan, 'Sex and the City' actor		Hand-held piece of armour ▶						

38

Move to music	▼	Brochure	Additional	▼	Person or thing beyond hope or help (coll)	Common garden insect	▼	Soft creamy French cheese
Hospital social worker ►		▼	▼			▼		Hands (out), as with justice, for instance
Gas used in lighting ►					Intent ►			▼
Blithe ►								
⚑					Savouring		Make free of ice	
Put off	Bit		Graham ___, author of 'The Third Man'	Periodic rise and fall of sea level	▼		▼	
Pin	▼		▼	Matures ►				
⚑						Beehive State of the USA		Conflict
Juicy fruit, such as lemon, orange, etc		Angry dispute		Layer of ground: a mat of grass and grass roots ►		▼		▼
Person to whom money is owed by a debtor ►		▼						
⚑				US space-flight agency (inits) ►				
Brittan, former Home Secretary	Heavy ►							

39

36

Top cards	Prop thrown in slapstick comedies (7,3)	Compass point at 67.5 degrees (inits)		Attribute	Having a wish for something	Brought up		Brought into existence
				Fall				
Ambi-guous								Expression of love
				Bathroom fixture				
Person who employs something		Wading bird					Arid regions of the world	
				Com-munists (coll)				
Clothing		Becomes ground down						
Provide (furniture) with a soft, padded covering		Sussex coastal town	Boy's name	Fat used in cooking		Russian emperor		Hoarfrost
US mid-western state					___ Lanka			
					Cash machine outside a bank (inits)			
At no time	Certify							

37

Game similar to bingo	All over	Named prior to marriage	▼	Woody core of a maize ear	Thinks unworthy of con-sideration	Go round and round	▼	List of dishes available
◣	▼	▼		Sketched ▶	▼	▼		
Rendition ▶								Brief periods of sleep
◣				Daze ▶				▼
Eager		Musical finale ▶					Relating to vehicles used on rough land (3-4)	
◣				At the summit of ▶			▼	
Novice		Short under-pants ▶						
Required		Outer garment	Engrave	Prophet		City in northern India		Deviates erratically from a set course
◣		▼	▼	▼		▼		▼
Memorisa-tion by repetition ▶					Indian state, capital Panaji ▶			
◣					Uncooked ▶			
Quiet	Fine cords of twisted yarn ▶							

Coin, a division of a Burmese kyat		Native North American tribe		Confirm	Have as a logical consequence		Expression used to frighten away animals	A single
Form of the Hebrew name of God							Not having any part cut or suppressed	
				Naming word				
Cloak-like, sleeveless garment	Inflammable liquid used as a solvent							
				Promotional notices (abbr)		Chest bone		Catch sight of
Rear, posterior part	Culinary plant		Buenos ___, capital of Argentina					
Leading caption of a newspaper article								
John ___, English poet, critic and dramatist		Hindu discipline	Entrance		Fatal disease of cattle (inits)			
						Ms Braun, Hitler's mistress		Desired result
Lout					Before, poetically			
Dreads, worries	Had one's revenge (3,4)							
					Put in			

39

Tolerate	Opulent	▼	'Terms of Endear-ment' star, ___ Winger	▼	Sea songs	▼	Common amphi-bians ___ Mrs Peron	▼
⌐					Of a female	►	▼	
Detest	Woman's support garment		Hurray! ___ Many times, poetically	►				
⌐	▼			Old horse ___ H Rider Haggard novel	►			
Lustre-less, not reflecting light		Rapid ___ More worn and shabby	►		▼		Narrow runner used for gliding over snow	
⌐		▼		That man's ___ Mark on the skin			▼	Shawls
Valuable fibre used for cords, carpets, etc	Debonair	Seven-day periods ___ Cotton fabric	▼					▼
⌐	▼	▼		Relax in a chair ___ Duelling sword	►			
Being of service ___ Missionary (5,4)	►				▼	Broadcast	Pot	
⌐						▼	▼	
Animal doctor ___ For each	►		Republic of Ireland	►				
⌐		Flower-less plants that reproduce by spores						

Country, capital Lima	▼	Arch	▼	Grandeur	▼	Common songbird of the thrush family	▼	Defamatory writing
Yielding a profit ►	▼							
Cane spirit ►				Regrets		Junk		Morally degraded, sleazy
┌			▼		▼			
Takes unawares	Important timber tree		Brother of one's father ►					
┌	▼				Exclamation		Mariner	
Domestic birds		Long-necked bird	Involuntary muscular contraction ►	▼			▼	
┌		▼		Neuter (a female cat, for example) ►				
City in the Asian part of Russia	Metal ring that opens a can		Throw	Sign of the zodiac		Playing card		Self-importance
Improbable story (4,4) ►	▼		▼	▼		▼		▼
┌					Sprocket ►			
Light narrow boat		Short jacket ►						

44

Deprive through death / Split up	⬛	Hide, animal skin	⬛	Go steady	⬛	Facts given	⬛	Disband
⬛		⬛						
Soften by soaking in water ▶				Compete		Discern-ment		Dissenter
Lifting device ▶				⬛		⬛		⬛
▶			Anticipate		Shortened forename of US president Lincoln ▶			
Charge levied on goods or services (inits)		Low-lying areas of eastern England	⬛				Intense dislike	
▶				Seventh letter of the Greek alphabet	Definite article ▶		⬛	
Coura-geous man	Feeble	Annul by rescinding ▶		⬛				
▶	⬛				Garden tool	Beard found on a bract of grass		Beast of burden
Young bird of prey		African desert ▶			⬛	⬛		⬛
▶			Is indebted to ▶					
Female panto-mime character		Improve-ments or correc-tions ▶						

45

Child's stringed toy (2-2)	▼	Large showy flower	▼	Crooked	▼	Breakfast rasher	▼	Anatomical structure resembling a horn in shape
Telephone switch-board assistant ►	▼						
Japanese currency unit ►			Secret look		Conclude by reasoning		Desig-nation
◣			▼		▼		▼
Issue regarded as poten-tially deba-table (4,5)	Afternoon meal		Boredom ►				
Uncouth ill-bred person ►	▼				Information reported in the papers		Full in quantity or extent
Birthday missive ►		Brings up	Go down on bended legs ►		▼		▼
◣	▼			Eagle ►			
Stiff, slightly lustrous synthetic fabric	Com-plexion		Fabric with prominent rounded crosswise ribs	Unisex name		Range of knowledge		Seize suddenly
◣	▼		▼	▼		▼		▼
Waste product useful as a fertiliser ►					Epoch ►		
Catch sight of ►					Bird's beak ►		

43

Coconut meat / Land turtle		Seek out and bring together (5,2)	Friar associated with Robin Hood		Plug in the mouth of a bottle	Spicy sauce to go with Mexican food		Brave man
								Adult male bird
Cause to flow					Continuous portion of a circle			
Irregular fold in an otherwise even surface					Toilet (coll)			
				Collective farm in Israel	Approach		Is able to	
Skein	Military dictators		Special way of doing something					
Girl's name						Belonging to the organ of smell		Having a smooth, soft surface
			Public announcement of a proposed marriage					
Container used for drinking		Cancelled	Woman's support garment (abbr)				Yoko ___, widow of John Lennon	
Bean curd					Roman god of the Sun			
			Show appreciation					
Branch of the British armed forces (inits)	Felt cap of Morocco				Irish digging tool			

Choice / Natives of Madrid, eg		Meantime / Direct		Under-ground cemetery		Graven images / Xmas card bird		Stalks of a plant
Small insecti-vorous bird / Schedule				Beep (a horn) / Girl's name				
Firedog		Abuse of foreigners / Records					British political party	
Periods of 60 minutes (abbr)	Muslim prayer leader / Insurgent					Mexican comrade		Country roads
Beige / Compulsion			Depend	Ancient Semitic deity / Spend				
				Qualification (inits) / Occupied a chair				
Strip the skin off	Associa-tion of sports teams							
				High rocky hills				

48

45

Fuel produced by the distillation of coal		Delivery from a plane or helicopter	19th letter / Married German woman		Fungal infection, tinea pedis (8,4)		Muscular, strong
Idiots					Seaman		
Cherry brandy						Suffered something unpleasant	
				Separate and distinct	Cricketing term (inits)		
Greek goddess	High ___, feeling of intense indignation						
Foresters	Dropsy		Absorb		Attempt		
							Acquiesce
Heroic					Body of salt water		
Barrier constructed to keep out the sea		Steffi ___, German tennis player				Flurry	
					Rowing pole		
Careless speed		Walked with long steps					
					Foot digit		

49

46

Passage-way	▼	Tipster	▼	Marries	▼	Invoice / Protective fold of skin	▼	Vase that usually has a pedestal or feet
▶		▼						Medical 'photo-graphs' (1-4)
Guest-house owner / Bar				Wild cat ▶ / Words of a book				▼
Steal cattle ▶				▼			God of love, also known as Cupid	
▶			All together, as a group (2,5)		Pasture ▶		▼	
Piece of metal held in a horse's mouth ▶		Termina-tion ▶	▼					
▶					___ and don'ts, rules of behaviour	▶		
Be valid		Male deer		Went first	▼	Preserve		Hair on a lion's neck
Makes damp	Cut-price events / Type of bird	▼				▼	Light brown	▼
▶	▼			Facts given ▶			▼	
Face covering / Racing sled	▶				Vehicle ▶			
▶			US film star and dancer, ___ Kelly ▶					

Failure	▼	Fugitive, escapee	Group noun for quails or larks	▼	Metropolis	Haywire	▼	Band associated with Damon Albarn
Relating to the eye socket ►	▼	▼				▼		Contradict
Edible fat ►				Mixture of earth and water ►				▼
Feeling of desire ►				Extreme anger ►				
►				Abominate	River of Russia and Kazakhstan		Add up	
Laugh loudly and harshly	Flour and water dough		Covered with a layer of fine powder	▼	▼		▼	
Writing material ►	▼					Text of a song		Ache, long
►			Saline ►			▼		▼
Alcove		Mr Garfunkel, singer-songwriter	One of the strands twisted together to make yarn ►				Old-fashioned affirmative answer	
Cab ►		▼			Scandinavian type of knotted pile rug ►		▼	
►			One who travels on the piste ►					
Armed struggle	Golf peg ►				Metal container ►			

51

48

Container for a bird	▼	Cook in a simmering liquid	▼	Box	▼	Largest member of the violin family (6,4)	▼	Indian ruler
Blessing ►	▼							
Indian state, capital Panaji ►				Girl's name	Race-course at which the Derby is run			Accepted
⌐			▼		▼		▼	
Pulse	Billiards stick		First letter of the Greek alphabet ►					
Tedious or unpleasant tasks ►	▼						Want strongly	
Listen		Forum in ancient Greece	Dwelling ►				▼	
∟		▼		Expression used at the end of a prayer ►				
Being the one previously mentioned	Short chain or ribbon on a pocket watch		Directed or controlled	Large deer		Behave		Directly or exactly, straight
∟	▼		▼	▼		▼		▼
By word of mouth ►					French vineyard or group of vineyards ►			
Financial institution ►					Golf peg ►			

52

49

Emblem	▼	Coffee shop	Print anew	▼	Person abroad to whom one regularly writes	▼	Piled	▼
◣					Female sheep	▶		
Divisions of the school year		Bobbin	Forename of golfer, Mr Woosnam	▶			Rub out	
◣		▼			Liveliness and energy	▶	▼	
Con-sumption	Join together by over-lapping		Cause anxiety or alarm	▶				
◣	▼		Mosque official		Boy			
Supplied, provided	▶		▼			City in central Japan on southern Honshu		Class of artistic endeavour
Com-petition		Piece of leather forming the upper of a shoe		Jump	Small barrel	▼		▼
◣		▼		▼			Common cyst of the skin	
Arrived	▶				Be in posses-sion of	▶	▼	
◣			Behind	▶				
Border of cloth stitched back	Drivel, trash	▶			A person in general	▶		

50

Italian mathematician, aka Leonardo of Pisa	Extreme mental retardation	Capital of West Germany 1949 to 1989	▼	Token that mailing fees have been paid (7,5)	▼	Behind schedule	▼	In operation
▶	▼	▼						
___ and don'ts, rules of behaviour ▶				17th letter of the Greek alphabet		Tubes		Bob ___, singer noted for his protest songs
Invulnerable to fear ▶						▼		▼
▶					Clinging plant ▶			
Old Testament prophet swallowed by a whale		Bible book telling the story of Christ ▶						
▶				Head of corn	Capital of Jordan		Golden ___, record popular in past times	
Dr Jekyll and Mr ___, R L Stevenson character	Copied	Lend flavour to ▶		▼	▼		▼	
▶	▼					Painting, sculpture, etc		Sum up
Any of various small breeds of fowl		Large fleet, especially of Spanish warships ▶				▼		▼
▶				Waterless ▶				
Microbe		Gasped for breath ▶						

54

51

Portable computer / Front of the head	▼	Biblical wife of Isaac / Incision	▼	Behave badly or cruelly towards	▼	English novelist / Currency units	▼	Italian poet (1265–1321)
◣		▼		Decorated with frosting ▶		▼		
Tavern ▶ / Alertness, vigilance				Couch / French word for 'black' ▶				
◣				▼				
'On the Origin of __', work by Charles Darwin	Ice-cream container ▶ / Attitude, beliefs							
◣		▼					Clothes-drying frames	
Sixth note in the tonic sol-fa scale	Girl's name ▶ / Bouquet					House for travellers	▼	Sloping mass of loose rocks at a cliff's base
◣	▼		Large floating mass of frozen water	Not that! / Female sheep ▶		▼		
Gown ▶ / Liquid used as a perfume			▼	▼	Imaginary monster ▶ / __ Maria			
◣					▼			
Sudden very loud noise	Be in awe of ▶							
◣				Additional ▶				

52

Elect		Covered entrance to a building		Microbe		All animal life of a place		Colloquial term for one's ancestry
Telephone switch-board assistant								
High rocky hill				Wading bird		Primitive plant forms		Dog ___, tattered
Bring to an end	Male cat		Light wood					
Native of Bangkok, for example					Native tribe of North America		Hispanic American	
Bullets, etc (abbr)		Masculine	Relative magnitude					
				Peruse text				
Illumined by a wax taper	Time period		Scheduled	Directed		Fair few?		Sheep in its second year
Sticky paste					Single number			
Observed sus-piciously					Fit out			

Tiny, common UK bird	▼	Large water jugs with wide spouts	▼	Declare formally as true	▼	Appliance that removes moisture	▼	Unfasten, remove pegs
Clergy-man's title ►		▼						
Lamb's mother ►				Clothing		Biting tools		Hidden supply
►				▼		▼		▼
Full of vim and vigour	Craft thought to be from space (inits)		Scene of action ►					
Former communist country (inits) ►	▼				Fit of shivering or shaking		Colour of ripe cherries	
Fearless and daring		Lariat	Consign-ment ►		▼		▼	
►		▼		Clarified butter used in Indian cookery ►				
Damage the reputation of	____ Lavender, Frank Pike in 'Dad's Army'		US TV company (inits)	Fish eggs		Invest with a knight-hood		Golf peg
►	▼		▼	▼		▼		▼
Yob deterrent (inits) ►					Application ►			
Organ of smell ►					Stinging insect ►			

54

Low dam		Before-hand	That man		Not as great in amount	Species of bacteria, a threat to food safety (1,4)	Daily news publica-tions	
Mayfly								
Sword lily					Island in French Polynesia, capital Papeete		Small tortilla topped with cheese	
Sulphur	Seized tightly		Aerodrome	Wing-shaped				
Drawings and photos in a book								
Quivering, shaky motion		Item of footwear		Lane down which a bowling ball is rolled		Asian country		Piece of music for nine instru-ments
Light-weight cotton with a corded surface							Pot	
Pocket billiards					Ask for overdue payment			
					Strong anger			
Rhythm in verse		Despot						

Girl's name	▼	Isolated from others — Curly lock	Insect resin — Buddy	▼	Pro-traction	▼	Aromatic herb	▼
◣		▼	▼		Metal-bearing mineral	▶		
Nicotinic acid ▶						Accord		
◣				Uncons-ciousness induced by drugs	Large wine cask or beer barrel ▶		▼	
County known as the Garden of England	Bona fide ▶			▼				
Sharply defined to the mind (5-3)	Paying guest		Clothes driers		Zero ▶			
◣	▼		▼					Bring to bear
Of or relating to the ear ▶					Affirmative word ▶			▼
Woman's name, old-fashioned		Embed-ded part ▶					Prompt	
◣					Frozen water ▶		▼	
Section of an orchestra	Quality of being extremely thorough ▶							
◣					Mesh ▶			

56

Boy's name		Ethnic group of Kenya and Tanzania		Measure (out)		Facing and with-standing with courage		Pigpens
Dish of beaten eggs								
Headgear				Small branch		Name of 16 kings of France		Hands out playing cards
Subject to change	Sound made by a cow		Of which person?					
Environ-mental condition							Portrait painter	
Lout		Drama set to music	Cook by radiated heat					
				Egyptian deity				
Affected by or full of grief	Not divisible by two		Unsound	Sense of self		Yoko ___, widow of John Lennon		Flow back
Pull, haul					Bird's beak			
Lower part of an interior wall					Sphere			

60

57

Part of a church which contains the altar	▼	German name for the Rhine river	▼	Honk (a horn)	▼	Ancient burial site	▼	Stony hillside
Artful or simulated sem-blance	►	▼						
H Rider Haggard novel	►			Anti-aircraft fire		Presen-tation, briefly	·	Low humming sound
►			▼		▼			▼
Cooked by immersing in fat or oil (4-5)	Measure of cloth		Person who avoids the company of others	►				
Fascin-ated, enthralled	► ▼						Medicinal plant	
Divulge confi-dential infor-mation		Central area of a Roman amphi-theatre	Holy book of Islam	►			▼	
►		▼		Traditional know-ledge	►			
Type of rug made from fleece and hide	Peppery		Former French gold or silver coin	Animal kept for compa-nionship		Case for containing a set of articles		Snare, trap
►	▼		▼	▼		▼		▼
Former	►				Decorate with frosting	►		
Subjected to great tension	►				Tit for ___, getting even	►		

58

Mountain transport system (5-3)	In existence	Nocturnal mammal	▼	Aviate	Trade	Fit for cultivation	▼	Country, capital Teheran
⌐	▼	▼			▼	▼		City in east-central France on the Rhone
Put in a horizontal position ►				By word of mouth ►				▼
⌐			Bunch of cords tied at one end	Numerous ►				
Morsel		Grave ►	▼				Invite	
⌐				Panache ►			▼	
Prefix meaning a million	Mrs Batty, in 'Last of the Summer Wine'	Emphasise ►						
Short message	▼	Instrument used in the course of work		In case		Device used to catch animals		Sign of something about to happen
⌐		▼		▼		▼	Title for a Turkish civil or military leader	▼
Part ►				Force by impact ►			▼	
⌐			Platform ►					
Chinese communist leader (1893–1976)	Illuminated ►			Wash off debris to separate precious minerals ►				

59

Use soap and water / Biblical tower	▼	Lady's bedroom or private sitting room	Ancient / Con-sequently	▼	Piece of folklore passed on verbally (3,5,4)	▼	Common name of the plant Euphorbia	▼
⌐		▼	▼		Circuit ►			
Seedy ►							Liquorice-flavoured seeds	
⌐			End-user	Armed struggle ►				
Hoodlum	Securing an arriving vessel with ropes ►		▼					
Fields of study	Fidel ___, Cuban socialist leader	Fertilised egg	Compete ►					
⌐	▼	▼						Search, as with a dragnet
Official symbols of a family, state, etc ►				Division of a tennis match ►				▼
Tempest	Sculpture of the head and shoulders ►					Gardening tool		
⌐				Expression of surprise or sudden realisation ►		▼		
Contributor	Colour ►							
⌐				Long and slippery fish ►				

63

60

Frighten away	▼	Dental filler	Titled peer of the realm	▼	Mounds raised to prevent flooding	Place out of sight	▼	Vagrant
West Indian song ▶		▼				▼		Sea vessel
In a murderous frenzy ▶					Flow back ▶			▼
Under-done ▶					Make the sound of a dove ▶			
▶					Curse		Watched	
Blends	___ del Sol, popular Spanish resort		Less than average tide	George ___, footballer who died in 2005	▼		▼	
Musical setting for a religious text ▶	▼		▼					Authoritative declaration (3-2)
▶				Information reported in the papers ▶				▼
Heavy book		Added to		Artful		Incision	Brazilian port, ___ de Janeiro	
Bathroom fixtures ▶	▼		▼		Weep ▶	▼	▼	
▶		Name of 16 kings of France ▶						
Measure of proficiency in judo	Time between sunrise and sunset ▶				Also ▶			

61

Confused mixture of things	▼	Region bordering Israel and Egypt	Native of northern Scandinavia	▼	Increased in size	▼	Nutrient	Whole
⌐					▼		Network of rabbit burrows	▼
Modify one's opinion to one less strong		Stocky short-legged harness horse	Move about in a predatory way ▶				▼	
⌐								
Informal term for a British policeman	Aromatic, edible bulb		Respire	Evergreen tree		Concealed		Itinerant Australian labourer
⌐	▼		▼	▼	Periods of 60 minutes (abbr)	▼		▼
Band of inelastic connective tissue		Appraisal ▶						
⌐					Chemical which carries genetic info (inits) ▶			
Entangle-ment		Abbreviation for the tenth month		Digestive juice secreted by the liver	⌐	Beverage	Sin	
⌐		▼		Single article ▶		▼	▼	
Poker stake	Acute intestinal infection ▶							
⌐			Take home ▶					

62

Random	Dwell	Thai currency unit	▼	Brand name of a ballpoint pen	▼	River of Russia and Kazakhstan	▼	Command given by a superior
⌐	▼	▼						
Organ of hearing ►				Con-sumption		Avoid by a sudden quick movement		Straps used to control a horse
Bear, carry a burden ►				▼		▼		▼
⌐			Pair of earphones	Material from which metal is extracted ►				
Egg of a louse		Leader ►	▼				Egg on	
⌐				Shoddy or tasteless articles	Alcoholic spirit flavoured with juniper ►		▼	
Measure (out)	Friendly nation	Capital of Greece ►	▼					
⌐	▼				Master Weasley, friend of Harry Potter	Also		Mr Selleck, who starred in 'Magnum PI'
Black and white mammal		Narrow channel of the sea ►			▼	▼		▼
⌐				Aware of ►				
Colour of the rainbow		Bicycle for two ►						

Corrode, as with acid	After that	Part of the eye	▼	Onerous task	Work very hard	Backless slippers	▼	Japanese form of wrestling
◣	▼	▼		Com-placent ►	▼	▼		
Aggressive and violent young criminal ►								Rod Hull's famous bird
Wander from a direct course ►				Succulent plant ►				▼
◣							Muham-mad ___, former boxer	
Disturb the composure of	Took notice of		On time	Epic tale	◣		▼	
◣	▼		▼	▼	Biblical twin of Jacob	Carries, conveys		Time of life between the ages of 13 and 19
Lads		Burrowing animal ►				▼		▼
◣					Expire		French word meaning 'me'	
Free from mist		Title used for a married French-woman ►			▼		▼	
◣				Magnetic metallic element, symbol Fe ►				
Car suitable for travelling over rough terrain		Disser-tation ►						

Adult male bird	▼	One who makes and serves coffee	Took food ___ Muslim prayer-leader	▼	Exceeding or sur-passing usual limits	▼	En-visioned	▼
Notice of some-one's death (abbr)	►	▼	▼		Outer edge of a plate	►		
Equip-ment for taking pictures	►						Line spoken by an actor to the audience	
⌐				Duck-billed creature	Henpeck	►	▼	
Gumbo	Stalemate	►		▼				
Located	Humor-ously sarcastic		Modernise		El ___, hero of a Spanish epic poem	►		
∟	▼		▼					Run off to marry
Wholly absorbed as in thought	►				Named prior to marriage	►		▼
Remove a lid		Stained with a colourant	►				Singing couple	
∟					Former name of the capital of Japan	►	▼	
Longs for		Make a showing (4,2)	►					
∟					Pedal digit	►		

68

Plays, theatre	▼	Immortal	Put baggage and provisions on a ship	▼	Invokes evil upon	'On the Origin of ___', work by Charles Darwin	▼	Exploit
Regress ►		▼	▼					Gait
Speck ►					Worthless or over-simplified ideas ►			▼
Nasty ►					Seventh letter of the Greek alphabet ►			
┏━					Cliff-dwelling, gull-like seabird		Stain	
Missives used as birthday or Christmas greetings	Shaped and dried dough		Runners used for gliding over snow	Face	▼		▼	
Device for opening several locks ►	▼		▼					Senior member of a group
┏━				Employed ►				▼
Travel by foot		Make a mistake		Woollen cap of Scottish origin		That chap	Alias (inits)	
Examination ►		▼		▼	Grass used as fodder ►	▼	▼	
┏━			Equally ►					
At a great distance	Male sheep ►				Adult male person ►			

66

Devoutly religious	Norse god of mischief	▼	Savoury jelly	▼	Send from one place to another	▼	Cas-seroles / Playing card	▼
◣					Renegade ▶		▼	
Russian pancake	Collection of rules imposed by authority		Location / Take into custody ▶					
◣	▼		▼		Novel / Spread hay ▶			
Piece of lint used to apply medi-cation	Divisions of a play / French dramatist ▶				▼		Small coin	
◣		▼		Units used in printing / Skating jump ▶			▼	Expresses in words
Very light, rich pastry	Runs with great speed		Farewell remark / Deficient in beauty ▶	▼				▼
◣	▼				Disap-proving expression / Cereal ▶			
Hand tool for boring holes / Glorious						Com-pletely	Hard-shelled fruit of a tree	
◣					▼		▼	
Cambs cathedral / Burned remains	▶			Hint ▶				
◣			Changes from a solid to a liquid state ▶					

70

Ms Myskow, TV star	Word expressing a motion towards the centre	Almost	▼	Utters in an irritated tone	Extremely savage	Entomb, especially after cremation	▼	Over-worked horses
	▼	▼		Small medicine bottle ►	▼	▼		
Making a structure in which to lay eggs ►								Edgar Allan ___, US writer and poet
Bathroom fixture ►				Division between signs of the zodiac ►			▼	
►							Signal to do something	
Swift pirate ship	Moving in a single direction (3-3)		Acid found in vinegar	Former ►			▼	
►	▼		▼	Kimono sash		Apportion		Behave towards
Spanish artist (1746-1828)		Treat with excessive indul-gence ►		▼		▼		▼
►					Tool for driving or forcing something by impact		Strident noise	
Famous person (abbr)		Violent denun-ciation ►			▼		▼	
►				Elaborate song for a solo voice ►				
Follower of Hitler	Con-stituent of concrete ►							

71

68

Reached a destination	Prevent from breathing	Extinct flightless bird of New Zealand	▼	Making warm	Long under-ground tube for oil, gas, etc	Feeling of ill-will arousing active hostility	▼	Indication
⌐	▼	▼		Cleared a debt ▶	▼	▼		
Drenching ▶								Basic monetary unit of Bangla-desh
⌐				British imperial capacity measure ▶				▼
Ejected saliva from the mouth	Individual unit ▶						Eldest son of Elizabeth II	
⌐				Chance, fortune ▶			▼	
Greenish-blue ▶	Japanese woman trained to entertain men ▶							
Small red fruit ▶	Seat for more than one person	Trudge	Shed bodily fluid		Estimate the value			Longings
⌐	▼	▼	▼		▼			▼
Charge ▶				Alcoholic brew ▶				
⌐				Cardinal number ▶				
English writer	Speak to ▶							

69

Wager	▼	Showy, flowering garden plant	▼	Scratches left by a glacier on rocks	Medicine that induces vomiting	▼	Independent ruler or chieftain	Unit of sound intensity
Hold in high regard ►	▼				▼		Characterised by great caution	▼
⚑				Small rodents ►		▼		
Celestial body	Free-handed ►							
⚑				Artificial hairpieces		Reinstate		Grades, stages
Female operatic star	Long dress		Fitted with cables	▼	▼			▼
Transducer used to measure light (5,3) ▼								
Person who explains or interprets something		Left side of a ship	Singles		Golf club with a relatively narrow metal head		Expel	
⚑	▼		▼		▼		▼	
Electrically charged particle ►				Dissolute man in fashionable society ►				
Painting, sculpture, music, etc	Contrition ►							
⚑				Meshes ►				

73

Nelson ___, South African former president		Detest	Assist		Food store		Jar for flowers	Important North Atlantic food fish
							Cut-price events	
Counter-pane		Point	Lariat					
Instrument measuring height above ground	Downwind		Deadlock	Berth		Lottery game		Go backwards
Musical pace		Sour-tempered						
				Gentle utterance to call someone's attention		Pause during which things are calm		
Young girl		Fit for cultivation						
			Period of time					
Boundary		Carapaces						
			Capital of the Maldives					

74

71

Sheets and pillowcases (3-5)		Genuine		Tear violently		Mouse-like rodent / Smaller in amount		In an unpalatable state
Human/canine monster / Hideout				Went / Decorated with frosting				Imposed a levy
Women								Character depicted in Piccadilly Circus
			Come-back		Either of male or female			
Be unwell		Be in awe of						
					Fishing implement			
Offensively malodorous		Mammal with a long coat and strong claws		'Father ___', TV sitcom		Emotion of strong affection		Place in the post
Sufferings, troubles	Intestine / Judo belt						Fasten	
				Show excessive affection				
Washtub / Nearly hopeless				French word for 'wine'				
				Pip				

75

72

Act that avoids a loss of dignity (4-5)	▼	Thin slice of toast with savoury food	▼	Regenerate / Hindu dress	▼	Decree that prohibits something	▼	Similar things placed in order
⌐				▼				
Highland pole		Grand-mother ▶				As a result		Homework
⌐				Gratuity / Wood plant ▶	▼			▼
Moldovan monetary unit		Shrivel / Accepted practice ▶		▼				
⌐		▼	Dreamlike state	Ploy / Make less effective ▶				
Exclama-tion of dismay (4,2)	Pigpens ▶		▼	▼			Small flock of grouse or partridge	
⌐						Musical finale	▼	Naked
Battle-ground	Breach / Fish eggs ▶				Adult male swan ▶	▼		▼
⌐	▼				Egg cells ▶			
Postpone	Fragment of incom-bustible matter left from a fire ▶							
⌐					Affirmative word ▶			

76

Distinctive quality	River flowing into the Caspian Sea	Cause extensive destruction	▼	One who drives cars at high speeds	Not affected by alcohol	Large group or crowd	▼	Hindu princess
▶	▼	▼		Make a pretence	▶	▼		
Nocturnal mammal native to North America	▶							Alliterative term for a young woman
Rever-ential salutation	▶			Ship's prison	▶			▼
▶							Flightless Australian bird	
Struck with fear or appre-hension	Drill used to shape or enlarge holes		Trousers that end above the knee	Fork prong	▶		▼	
▶	▼		▼	▼	Bobbin	Graph		Com-ponents
Peak		Symptom of indi-gestion	▶			▼		▼
▶					School group (inits)		Promis-sory note (inits)	
Conduc-ting stick		Fix	▶		▼		▼	
▶				Canter	▶			
Departed, went		Position	▶					

77

Dried seed used in soup (5,3)	Recipient of money	Be in a horizontal position	⬛	Badly lit	Line of descent of a pure-bred animal	One who leaves to live abroad	⬛	Blonde
								Easily irritated
Aspire				Expel (gases or odours)				
			Fairy	Cala-mitous				
Cheerio		Gulp					Kind	
				Gravel				
Honk	Group of islands, capital Suva	Not often						
Number represented by the Roman XV		Affec-tionate, loving		Looked at		Carpentry pin		Make tea
							School group (inits)	
Australian term for a young kangaroo					Abbrevia-tion for the fourth month			
			Class of people enjoying superior status					
Garbage container	Informal term for a father				Collection of rules imposed by authority			

75

Food made of curdled soybean milk		Repeat performance		Footprint		Capable of being detected		Asian peninsula
Adhering to what is commonly accepted								
Professional price				Memorisation by repetition		Grasslike marsh plant		Grunt
Takes unawares	Israeli sub-machine-gun		Huge sea					
Combined							Motor	
US coin	Scottish mountain of at least 3,000 feet	Avid						
			Twisted					
Illumined by a wax taper	The alphabet (inits)		Dull	Field suitable for grazing by livestock		Impudent or insolent rejoinder		Explosive compound (inits)
Soft creamy French cheese					Hostelry			
Unconscious state					Caress gently			

79

76

Rate of travel (inits)	▼	Fail to fulfil a promise	▼	Multipli-cation	▼	Short jacket	▼	Type of food shop (abbr)
Captive ▶	▼							
▶			American mother		Kitchen range		Perspira-tion	
Those people	Goddess of retribution ▶		▼		▼		▼	
Holiday town ▶						Earnest		
Profes-sional cook	Fairground game of ring throwing (4-2)	Large deer ▶			▼			
◣	▼		◤	Demon	By means of ▶			
Not affected by alcohol		Sculpture of the head and shoulders	County known as the Garden of England ▶					
◣		▼		Trap made by an arachnid	Chafe			Move the head in agreement
Humorous play on words ▶			Small bird ▶	▼	▼			▼
Hallucino-genic drug (inits) —— Chapeau	▶		Basic unit of currency in Germany ▶					
◣			Flowed back ▶					

77

Cylinder	USA's 'Mormon State'	Short jacket	▼	Instrument played with a bow	Government income due to taxation	Agent which assists colonic irrigation	▼	Was present, is now gone
⌐	▼	▼		Marsh plant	▼	▼		
Colourless flammable liquid used as a solvent ►								Unit of weight equivalent to 2240 pounds
Entirely ►			Air-hole ►				▼	
⌐						Abbreviation for the fourth month		
Proposition, idea	Oriental tobacco pipe with a long tube		System of news-groups on the internet	Indian bread, baked in a clay oven ►			▼	
⌐	▼		▼	Former Hollywood star, ___ Lupino		Advance		Having the leading position
Archaic form of the word 'you'		Long jagged mountain chain ►		▼		▼		▼
⌐				Seaman		By way of		
Motorised bicycle		Indigenous person ►			▼		▼	
⌐				Region regularly afflicted by monsoons ►				
Austen, English author	Fibre ►							

Large and often sumptuous tent	▼	Country, capital Bamako	Clump	▼	British nobleman	▼	Simple, bare	Precious or semi-precious stone
◣							Heavy open wagon	▼
Occurring in the centre of a river		Put on	Play charac-terised by broad satire	►			▼	
◣								
Extremely ornate	Dwelling		Popular British cheese	Sweet potato		Chest for the Covenant		Cleaning implement
◣	▼		▼	▼	'Hole-in-the-wall' cash machine (inits)	▼		▼
____ pole, tribal emblem		Dense growth located on the head, eg	►				Arm off of a larger body of water	
◣					Slumber (coll)	►	▼	
Peruse		Muham-mad ___, former boxer		Diagram-matic repre-sentations of roads	▼		Woman's garment	Centre
◣		▼		Adept	►		▼	▼
Dam	Primitive freshwater creature	►						
◣				Fill to satis-faction				

Port city in southern Kenya	▼	Con-sistency	Wallop	▼	Block consisting of a thick piece of something	▼	Placed in position	Overnight conden-sation
▼				▼		Deep-bodied North Pacific salmon	▼	
Type of make-up		Former French gold or silver coin	Cut into pieces	►			▼	
▼		▼						
Evil or corrupt practice	Makes indistinct		Marine plant	Work unit		Constric-ting snake		Court
▼	▼		▼	▼	Knot with two loops and loose ends	▼		▼
Russian prison camp for political prisoners		Therefore	►				Fraught with risk	
►					Flurry	►	▼	
Small area of land		Cricketing term (inits)		Unfor-tunately	▼	Excessive, extreme (inits)		Poem intended or adapted to be sung
►		▼		Slang term meaning insane or very stupid	►	▼		▼
Exhibiting lustful desires	After the expected or usual time	►						
►				Eyelid swelling	►			

83

State of deep uncons- ciousness	Musical instrument	Mode of procedure	▼	Gentle- man's gentleman	Course	Shar- pened	▼	Charter
◤	▼	▼		Flightless bird of South America	▼	▼		
Inflatable bag ◣								Known
Number ◣				Old word meaning 'in the direction of' ◣				▼
◤							Strong, angry emotion	
Having toothlike projec- tions	Number represen- ted by the Roman XI		Fried potato slices	Creature said to live in the Himalayas	◤		▼	
◤	▼		▼	▼	Prepare for printing	Burn		Prospect
Clemency		Employs more than once ◣				▼		▼
◤					Went in advance		Alliterative term for a young woman	
Accord or comport with		Fodder harvested while green ◣			▼		▼	
◤				Panache ◣				
Shed tears		Bicycle seat ◣						

81

Police (coll)	Gemstone	Roof of the mouth	▼	Until now (2,3)	Petty officer on a ship	Espresso coffee with milk	▼	Dandy
⌐	▼	▼		Band associated with Damon Albarn ▶	▼	▼		
Goods carried by a large vehicle ▶								Coaster
Alcoholic beverage ▶				Part of a flower ▶				▼
⌐							Be unwell	
At top speed (4,3)	News chief		Crumple	Expression of dislike	⌐		▼	
⌐	▼		▼	▼	Clean or orderly	Means of communi-cation (abbr)		Eliminate from the body
Deciduous tree	Small wave on the surface of a liquid ▶					▼		▼
⌐					Peppery		Go fast	
Homes for bees	On land ▶				▼		▼	
⌐				Burden ▶				
Foreman		Degree ▶						

85

Male pig	▼	Push	▼	Blackleg	▼	Narrow escape from danger (5,5)	▼	Upstairs storage space
Kiss ►	▼							
Norwegian pop group (1-2)				Musical com-position		Mr Charles, of 'Red Dwarf' fame		Judder
►				▼		▼		▼
Long flexible snout	Asso-ciation of criminals		Roost ►					
Gorgon whose hair consisted of snakes ►	▼						Former commu-nist country	
Shoe with a cross-strap on the upper (1-3)		Bright blue	Avoid one's assigned duties ►				▼	
►	▼			Fever ►				
Compass point at 135 degrees (5-4)	Awkward, stupid person		Be equal, draw	Owned		Fitting		Number
►	▼		▼	▼		▼		▼
Opera song ►					Food wrapped in a pastry shell ►			
Feast upon ►					Bronze ►			

Contented, pleased	▼	Round objects used in games	▼	Seizes with the teeth	Assistant	▼	Boundary, rim	▼
◣								
In another location		Certain		For what reason?	Rushed, hurried		Dangerous	
◣		▼		▼	▼		▼	
Japanese dish ►						Able to be heard		Adolescent
Poem intended or adapted to be sung	Excitement		Agent used in fermenting beer	►		▼		▼
◣	▼		Public transport vehicle	British peer of the highest rank ►				
Japanese warrior		Measure (out)	▼	Feeling of intense anger	Colouring agent ►			
◣	▼			▼			Uncooked	
Flat tableland with steep edges ►					Woman's garment (abbr) ►		▼	
►			Russian prison camp for political prisoners ►					
Item of equipment used in baseball	Compass point at 67.5 degrees (inits) ►				Ram's mate ►			

84

Link up, connect (3,2) / Gall	▼	Country road	▼	Poetry	▼	Word of laughter (2-2) / Declines	▼	DNA unit / Marine plant
◣		▼		Inspires wonder in ►		▼		▼
Trans-ducer for converting signals to sounds ►								
___ and outs ►				Domain / Cowboy exhibitions ►				
◣				▼	Member of an orchestra		Astral	
Curl of the lip	Crusta-cean with seven pairs of legs	Sharpens (a razor)	Abnor-mally fat	◣	▼		▼	
◣	▼	▼	Italian poet (1265–1321) / Break	◣				
Belonging to him / Empha-sised ►			▼					
US chocolate biscuits ►						Constric-ting snake		Augment
Capable of happening or existing ►						▼		▼
Choose / Public promotions (abbr) ►			Drench ►					
◣			Look at intently					

88

85

Ponder	Egg on	Bracing atmosphere by the coast (3-3)		Slightest	Grotesque	Clock that wakes a sleeper at a preset time		Purchases
				Drag				
In a punctual manner								Chapeau
Carbon dioxide, for example				Hyphen				
							Nickname of US president Eisenhower	
Atmospheric condition	Ground surrounded by water		Apprehend	Exclude				
				Increases		Space created by the swing of a scythe		Lock of hair
Former unit of money in Italy		Brown with a reddish tinge						
					Duvet warmth rating		Small insectivorous bird	
Drink noisily		Demesne						
				Mr Redding, singer				
Printing fluids		Knit hose covering the lower part of the body						

86

Tibetan or Mongolian priest		Music of the early 20th century	Owned — Estimation		To a great extent or degree		Draw back, as with fear or pain	
Elaborate song for a solo voice					Belonging to us			
Enrage							Harden	
				Expose one's body in order to get a tan	' ___ City', 2005 film			
Container for a bird	Savouring							
Perfume in the form of a ball	Expression of sorrow (2,4)		Apprehend		Directly or exactly, straight			
								Light-weight triangular scarf
Aromatic plant					Umpire (abbr)			
Cap made of soft cloth		Pro ___, in proportion					Hoot with derision	
					Television company of the UK (inits)			
Animal		Battle of the US Civil War (1862)						
					Second person singular			

87

			▼				▼	
Finishing line for a foot race	Highest level attainable	Protruding abdomen		Des-patches	Becomes tired	Dissident		___ Austen, author of 'Mansfield Park'
▶	▼	▼		Enfold ▶	▼	▼		
Workers' dining hall ▶								___ and don'ts, rules of behaviour
Soft wet earth ▶				In one's sleeping place ▶				▼
▶							Side sheltered from the wind	
Harsh criticism or dis-approval	Brief sleep		Emer-gence	Ailments ▶			▼	
▶	▼		▼	Receptacle for ashes after a cremation		Clicks smartly		Fashion
Throb dully	Piece of material inset to enlarge a garment ▶			▼		▼		▼
▶					Dupe, swindle		Witness	
Ringo ___, former Beatle		Enclose in ▶			▼		▼	
▶				Exposed ▶				
Establish-ments where alcohol is served		Perceived, felt ▶						

88

Central Hawaiian island	▼	Reflective road stud (4-3)	That girl / Cloud	▼	Force released by nuclear reaction (6,6)	▼	Brief sleep	▼
Highest level attainable		▼	▼		Drink made by infusing dried leaves			
Coiffure ►							Chemically inactive	
�			Technician who produces moving cartoons	Sort period of time (abbr) ►		▼		
Hard fruits	Enduring strength and energy ►	▼						
Person who travels in a stolen vehicle	Of a sphere, flattened at opposite sides	▼	Cause extensive destruction	Large edible mushroom ►				
�			▼					Songs of praise
Long thick piece of wood ►				To the ___ degree (to the utmost) ►				▼
Measure of gold's purity	Long depression in the surface of the land ►					Edgar Allan ___, US writer and poet		
�				Number of turns in 60 seconds (inits) ►		▼		
German conductor and composer of operas	Monster of which Medusa was a type ►							
�				Affirmative answer ►				

92

Bart Simpson's father	▼	Trailer equipped with living quarters	At another time	▼	Peak	One put forward for election	▼	Fête
Egg-shaped and flutey-toned instrument		▼	▼			▼		Even score at the end of a game
Hair on an animal's neck	▶				Elderly	▶		▼
Character depicted in a statue in Piccadilly Circus	▶				Spoil	▶		
⌐					Lass		Plural of the word 'am'	
Allow	Delivery	Mixture of fat and flour used as a basis for sauces	Chew	▼			▼	
Object that impedes free movement	▼		▼					Artificial
⌐			Ridge of rock, coral, etc	▶				▼
Floor covering (abbr)		Unit of electric current (abbr)		Extremely cold		Goon	Intense mournfulness	
Public passenger vehicle	▶	▼		▼	Nocturnal bird	▶	▼	
⌐			Confusion, disarray	▶				
Unit of electrical resistance	Settle a bill	▶			Fixed charge for a professional service	▶		

Capital of Tibet	Large and imposing manor	▼	Strong, lightweight wood	▼	Rough	▼	Military trainee / Rerid	▼
◣					Woman's support garment ▶		▼	
Small compartments	Long and slippery fish		Ghastly / Segment of a tree trunk ▶					
◣	▼		▼		Monkey / Colourful, ornamental fish ▶			
Horse fly		Long-living trees / Consider in detail ▶					Pasture	
◣		▼	Lubricant / Phonograph record ▶				▼	Area set back or indented
Yellowish-brown colour	Fast-running, long-eared mammals		Frogman / Type ▶	▼				▼
◣	▼		▼		Centre / Cylindrical grain tower ▶			
Wrong / Basic truth or law ▶						Level	Destiny	
◣						▼	▼	
Bring to a close / Employ ▶			Commu-nist state of Asia					
◣			Harbours ▶					

91

Deficient in beauty		Girl's name	Do something		Super-fluous, redundant		Gesture	Not many
Midge					UN finance and banking agency (inits)			
Inter-weaving							Drama set to music	
					At once			
City in central Japan on southern Honshu	Despise		Cathedral priest		British system of medical care (inits)	Salary given to an employee who is ill (4,3)		Lair
Gave per-mission to, authorised								
Farm outbuilding		Colloquial term for one's ancestry		Rent				
				Examine hastily				
Instrument					Incline		Decorate with frosting	Fetch
Sharpen (a blade)					Domestic swine			
			Quickly					
Drenched with water	'___ City', 2005 film				All the same			

Cere-monial dinner party	▼	Green gemstone	Immense	▼	Makes a mistake	▼	Cease	Animal doctor (abbr)
⌐					▼		___ stick, plaything propelled by jumping	▼
Container with a perforated lid used at table		Popular vegetable	Fumble ►				▼	
⌐		▼						
Animal related to the giraffe	Ms Minogue		Appealing to many	Extreme anger		Trot		Yelp
⌐	▼		▼	▼	Delight ►	▼		▼
Run off	Approxi-mately (2,2) ►					Fine cords of twisted fibres		
⌐				Pain or discomfort ►		▼		
Distribute playing cards	Reveren-tial salutation		Colour of un-bleached linen	▼	Implement used to propel or steer a boat		Seventh letter of the Greek alphabet	
⌐	▼		Central part ►		▼		▼	
Affirm	Tramp ►							
⌐			___ Major, the Great Bear con-stellation ►					

Large, hairy, tropical spider	▼	Gateaux	▼	Native New Zealander	Three-dimensional shape	▼	Decoy, lure	▼
Jollity		Fast-running and flightless bird		Brother of George Gershwin	Office note		Daughter of a sibling	
		▼		▼	▼		▼	
County	►					Mass of precious metal		Horizontal plant stem
By means of	Adult insect		Deep yellow colour	►		▼		▼
	▼		Unit of sound intensity	Expression of pain	►			
Situated at or extending to the side		Finishing line for a foot race	▼	Feeling of intense anger	Garland of flowers	►		
		▼		▼			Female deer	
Fête	►				Artificial language, a simplification of Esperanto	►	▼	
			Atmosphere of depression	►				
Early form of modern jazz	Stretch	►			Named prior to marriage	►		

Behind schedule	Com-petent	Maker and alterer of garments	▼	Italian operatic composer (1813-1901)	Fibre used for making rope	Very recently	▼	Airborne soldier
◤	▼	▼		Hitch, unfore-seen problem ◂		▼		
Object that impedes free movement ◂								Ta-ta
Saucepan cover ◂				Wash with a mop ◂				▼
◤							Repent	
In the shape of a coil	Unimpor-tant details		Item applied to reduce swelling (3,3)	Strip the skin off	◤		▼	
◤	▼		▼	▼	Ancient Greek harp	Retch		Bill for an amount due
Disrobe		Seal of approval ◂				▼		▼
◤					Adversary		Chap	
Motor-cycle rider		Happen to ◂			▼		▼	
◤				Egg-shaped ◂				
Capital of Peru		Avaricious ◂						

Large luxurious car (abbr)	▼	Variety of mandarin orange	Catalogue	▼	Marry	▼	Financier	Combined stakes of the betters
Offshore area ►		▼	▼		Enquire ►			▼
Cricket over in which no runs are scored ►							Asinine	
▶				Israeli sub-machine-gun	Case containing a set of articles ►	▼		
Plenty	Pupil ╲			▼				
Hollow under the upper limb	Annul by rescinding		Attractive		Beam (of light) ►			
◢	▼		▼			Dark reddish-brown		Hinged lifting tool
Fruiting spike of a cereal plant ►			Put baggage and provisions onto a ship	Collection	▼		▼	
Right-hand page	If not, then ►		▼				Added to	
◢				Greek deity, half man, half goat ►		▼		
Harold ___, silent movie actor	Not easily borne, wearing ►							
◢				Public promotions (abbr) ►				

Tiring routine with no time for rest (3,4)	▼	Level to the ground	Flexible containers	▼	Ready money	▼	House attached to one other	Truck with an enclosed cargo space
◣					▼		Be active	▼
Period of economic decline		Sound made by a dove	Greek letter ▶				▼	
◣		▼						
Distinctive period of time	Means of communi- cation		Cupboard	Con- spicuous success		Cut wood		Scottish port
◣	▼		▼	▼	Expanse of salt water ▶	▼		▼
Uncer- tainty		Verdi opera with an Egyptian theme ▶					Acquiesce	
◣					Hostilities ▶		▼	
Edible legu- minous seed		'Much ___ about Nothing', Shakespe are play		Female domestic	▼	Israeli sub- machine- gun		Social insect
◣		▼		Halo ▶		▼		▼
Fired a bullet at	Inhabitant ▶							
◣			Prescribed selection of foods ▶					

Bringing death	▼	Conveyance attached to a motorcycle	Ku Klux ——, secret society	▼	Date-producing trees	Cupboard	▼	Bill of fare
With a side or oblique glance	▼	▼	▼			▼		Name given to 6 June 1944 (1-3) ▼
Cash register					Added to ►			
Biblical first man					Sprout ►			
►					Drum out		Grazing land	
Scottish valleys	Infectious disease		Quantity of paper	Alone	►		▼	
Large and often sumptuous tent	▼		▼					Bread-raising agent ▼
►				Halt ►				
Heal		Consumption		Boat built by Noah		Angry	Curious	
American feline	►	▼		▼	Extinct flightless bird of New Zealand ►	▼	▼	
►			Interprets words ►					
Donkey	Expression of surprise or mild alarm	►			Banned insecticide (inits) ►			

Hidden storage space	▼	Person's manner of walking, pace	▼	Destiny, fate	▼	Continent — Very spicy sauce of peppers	▼	Private box in a theatre — Moisture
▶			▼	Put away for storage ▶		▼		▼
Epic tale — Horse-drawn vehicle	▶							
That man ▶				Assist to do wrong ▶ — Walk silently				
▶				▼	Highly seasoned meat stuffed in a casing		Small guitar with four strings	
Disturb, especially by minor irritations (3,2)	Circum-vented	Passen-gers	Bring out an official document ▶		▼		▼	
▶	▼	▼	Bundles ▶ — Cereal grass					
Of a female — Good ▶			▼					
Farewell remark ▶		—				Cut wood		Informal term for a father
Expired ▶						▼		▼
Before — Public promotions (abbr) ▶				Fête ▶				
▶			Stitched ▶					

99

		Rower	Type of fat		Papas	Mother-of-pearl		Portuguese city in the Algarve
Girl's name								
Exclamation of praise to God								Ditch around a castle
Praise or glorify					Limb			
Metal-containing minerals					Make the sound of a dove			
				'The ___', tragi-comic play by Shakespeare	Fabric made from the hair of sheep		Ms Cassidy, singer of 'Songbird'	
Compass point	Long-distance bus		Chirp					
Engraving in relief						Characteristic of song		Took part in an argument
			Grinding tooth					
Dupe, swindle		Direct	Provide in a continuous or insistent way				Alias (inits)	
Mantle					Not processed or refined			
			Long sharp-pointed implement					
22nd letter of the Greek alphabet	Vehicle test (inits)				Bounder			

103

Red dyestuff	Child who has lost both parents	Heal	▼	Clarified butter used in Indian cookery	▼	Against	▼	Shows concern
▼	▼	▼						
Regret ▶				Bovine sound		Erik ___, French avant-garde composer		Implement with a shaft and barbed point
Land and the buildings on it			▼			▼		▼
▶			Enclosed		Type of cobra ▶			
Her		Outer garment ▶	▼				Sticky plant fluids	
▶				Centre	Lyricist, ___ Gershwin ▶		▼	
Gen (abbr)	Affirm solemnly and formally as true	Decorative layer ▶		▼				
▶	▼				Rug	One of four playing cards in a deck		Snare, trap
Charac-terised by great caution		Stay ▶			▼	▼		▼
▶			Disease of the skin ▶					
Capital of Italy		Abhor ▶						

104

101

Distance to fuel consump-tion ratio (inits)	▼	Bower of climbing plants	▼	Plait hair	On a ship	▼	Archaic form of the word 'you'	Television company of the UK (inits)
Social outcast ►			▼		▼		Person with an out-standing intellect	▼
►				Explosive device ►			▼	
Old Mogul capital	Temporary camp used by soldiers ►							
►				Unbeliever		Mother of the ancient Irish gods		Lamb's mother
Having desirable qualities	Mass of ice		Livid ►	▼		▼		▼
Never before used (5,3)	▼							
Detractor		Country, capital Teheran	Diminutive		Unit of surface area (100 square metres) ►			
►		▼	▼			Visual receptor cell sensitive to light		Stake
Network ►					Chest bone ►	▼		▼
Tough sort of plastic	Woodland flower ►							
►					Once common insecticide (inits) ►			

105

102

Get up	▼	Wash	Stop / Ins and / details	▼	Bias (3-9)	▼	Scandi-navian kingdom	▼
Religious picture ▶	▼		▼		At present ▶			
Gunk, slime ▶							Rotund	
▶				Merry-go-round	Ground containing a mat of grass and grass roots ▶		▼	
Trotters, hooves, etc	Attribute ▶			▼				
Puts aside, earmarks	Online mags (1-5)		Printed mistakes		Hideout ▶			
▶	▼		▼					Fuses together
Nought ▶					Con-densed water vapour ▶			▼
Peruvian tribe at the time of the Spanish conquest		Irre-coverable state of devasta-tion ▶					Zodiacal Lion	
▶					Old cloth measure ▶		▼	
Common		Made fun of ▶						
▶					Distress signal (inits) ▶			

106

Bouquet		Archaeo-logical period (4,3)	Cut-price event		Trunk of a tree	Forbidden		Tolerable, indifferent (2-2)
Italian rice dish								Move back and forth
Examina-tion conducted by word of mouth					Donkey			
Small velvety-furred burrowing mammal					Decorative tie			
				Com-muniqué	European capital city once called Christiania		Loud noise	
Weather-cock	Drama which is sung		Morose					
Giants who like to eat human beings						Collection of maps		Slang for 'drunk'
			Tilt					
Monkey		One who is playfully mis-chievous	Chronic drinker				Burnt remains	
Capital of Latvia					Circuit			
			Drinking vessel					
Barrier which contains the flow of water	Edgar Allan ___, US writer and poet				Coconut ___, popular fairground stall			

104

Object used to start an explosion	Expensive white fur	Instrument	▼	Christmas	▼	Clubs used in the game of cricket	▼	Arrives
	▼	▼						
Fish eggs ►				Completely		Japanese dish		Grasslike marsh plant
Black treacle ►				▼		▼		▼
►			Low wall along the edge of a roof		Application ►			
Nothing		Added to ►	▼				Ailing	
►				Bladed chopping tool	Embrace ►		▼	
Salty Greek cheese	Distinctive and stylish elegance	Gorge ►		▼				
►	▼				Boy	Children's game		Cereal crop
Chill out	Annoy persistently ►			▼	▼		▼	
►			Containing an unusual amount of grease ►					
Female pantomime character		Entwine ►						

108

Monster	Pitney, US singer	Dried grape	▼	Aromatic plants used in cookery	Sorrow	Pleasantly cold and invigorating	▼	Roast
◣	▼	▼		Con-fidence trick	▼	▼		
Set aside ▶								Witness
Writing point of a pen ▶				Expires ▶				▼
◣							Enchant	
Morals, examples	Creature		Flee	Fencing sword ▶			▼	
◣	▼		▼	Steal from a person		Coral reef		Equine creature with black and white stripes
Stripe of con-trasting colour		Inferior substitute or imitation ▶		▼		▼		
◣				Definite article ▶ / Way to post (inits)				
Signalling word used to indicate com-pliance		Assimilate or take in ▶		▼				
◣				Resem-bling wings ▶				
Salve		Spanish rice dish ▶						

Land force	Stand up on the hind legs	Control	▼	Text of a song	Ricochet	Appropriate	▼	Makes a wager
⌐	▼	▼		Regretted ▶	▼	▼		
Ardently serious ▶								Likewise
Tropical black cuckoo of central America ▶				Sculpture of the head and shoulders ▶				▼
⌐						Prominent rock or pile of rocks on a hill ▼		
Farm vehicle	Walk silently	Prepared (a gun) for firing	As far as (2,2) ▶					
⌐	▼	▼		Gelid		Drive out		Skin covering the top of the head
Pace	Passengers ▶		▼			▼		▼
⌐					Wise bird	UN agency concerned with work (inits)		
Of the eye	Short-sightedness ▶				▼		▼	
⌐			Deep hole or shaft dug to obtain water ▶					
Augur	Small indefinite quantity ▶							

110

107

Ali ___ Markedly masculine		Musical setting for a religious text	Area for pans on a cooker — Name		Item used when pasting wallpaper (7,5)		Emoticon of a grinning face	
					Force by impact			
Cheap showy ornament							Give a speech	
				Special and significant stress	Roman god of the sun			
Produced tones with the voice	Building where plays are performed							
One of eight children born at the same time	Duplicator		Expresses in speech		Not of the clergy			Rock containing a cavity lined with crystals
Commitment to tell the truth					Sheep in its second year			
Makes reference to	Standard monetary unit of Bangladesh						Throughout time, poetically	
					Show displeasure vocally			
Alloy of copper and zinc	Looted							
					Earlier in time than, poetically			

111

Recent arrival	▼	Calf meat	▼	Professional charges	▼	Dried-up river bed / Rumour-monger	▼	Dry (wine)
		▼				▼		Ms Minogue
Drink / Tiny	▼			Prune / Cruise	▶			▼
French sweet black-currant liqueur	▶			▼			By an unknown author, in short	
▶			Swimmers	volatile, smelling salts	▶		▼	
High mountain pass		Woman's two-piece costume	▼					
▶				Edgar Allan ___, US writer and poet	▶			
Untamed		Thin strip of wood or metal		Colour	▼	Game on horseback		Amount owed
Opening into or through something	Woolly mammals / Type of poem	▼				▼	Small coin	▼
▶	▼			Give medicine to	▶		▼	
Have the courage / Makes a wager	▶				Propel in a high arc	▶		
▶				Boxing match	▶			

White substance beneath the peel of fruit	At rest	Military personnel	▼	Cloak, often knitted	Puts into a letterbox	Disorderly outburst (3-2)	▼	Female birds
▼	▼	▼		Sound made to indicate a bad smell	▼	▼		
Compel by threatening ▶								Morsel left at a meal, crumb
Depleted ▶				Neither good nor bad (2-2)	▶			▼
▶						Bruce ___, kung fu actor who died in 1973		
Artefact from the latter part of the Stone Age	Collection of beehives		Disease of the skin	Plenty ▶		▼		
▶	▼		▼	▼	Condiment, sodium chloride	Left over, superfluous		Moves in large numbers, swarms
Artist's tripod ▶		Foundation garment ▶				▼		
▶					Train driver's compartment		Fluid product of an inflammation	
Franz ___, Hungarian composer (1811-1886)		Break free ▶			▼		▼	
▶				Cuckoo pint, for example ▶				
Lip of a hat		Mother superior ▶						

110

Coffee-chocolate drink	▼	Verse form	▼	Former monetary unit of Finland	▼	Planet / City in Israel (3,4)	▼	Show affection / Interfering person
▸		▼		Particle ▸		▼		▼
Come to terms with / Building material ▸								
Adult female bird ▸				Wooden vehicle on runners ▸ / Keen				
▸				▼	Having the property to wear down gradually		Famous mountain	
Mythical monster similar to a vampire	Light tanker for supplying water or fuel	Smiles contemptuously	Make merry ▸		▼		▼	
▸	▼	▼	Ambition ▸ / Walking-stick					
US TV Co (inits) / Inspection (4-4) ▸			▼					
Brings on to solid food ▸					Grand-mother		Tolstoy, Russian writer	
Guard ▸					▼		▼	
Before / Periods of 60 minutes (abbr) ▸			Jar for flowers ▸					
▸			Slowly, in music ▸					

114

Type of cobra	▼	Australian term for food	▼	Lay out in a line	Noisy quarrel or fight	▼	Golfing pegs	Woman's garment (abbr)
Rake with machine-gun fire from a plane ►		▼			▼		Essential oil obtained from flowers	▼
►			Back end ►				▼	
Goad	Card game, a form of rummy ►							
►			Light drawn around the head of a saint ▼		City and lake in central Switzerland ▼		Dancer's one-piece costume ▼	
Very dark, black	Word denoting a person or thing	Conforming to Islamic dietary laws ►						
Cherish ►	▼							
Corruptible		Long strip of fabric	Back part of a foot		Finger-end protector		Phillips, Welsh actress	
◣	▼	▼		▼		▼		
Means of returning something by post (inits) ►			Operatic solo ►					
Cosmetic preparation used to darken the lashes	Meeting for an exchange of ideas ►							
◣			Let have for a limited time ►					

Container for keeping papers in order	Egyptian deity	Ransacked	▼	Take exception to	Female deity	Alphabetical listing of topics	▼	Blood-sucking parasite
⚑	▼	▼		Imperial capacity unit equal to 5 fluid ounces ►	▼	▼		
Unspecified person ►								Sweet potato ▼
Notice of intent to pay (inits) ►				Name given to 6 June 1944 (1-3) ►				
⚑							Expert	
With legs stretched far apart	Relating to the stars		Mass of snow permanently covering the land	Academic test (abbr) ►			▼	
⚑	▼		▼	Device used to propel a boat		Aligned oneself with		In that place ▼
Dried-up riverbed		Treat with excessive indulgence ►		▼		▼		▼
⚑					(They) exist		Cover with insulation to prevent heat loss	
Confused or unable to decide what to do (2,3)		Baby's bed ►			▼		▼	
⚑				Back end ►				
Mother		Deposit of personal property as security for a debt ►						

Dairy product / Cobbler	▼	Accounting entry / The act of watching	▼	Collection of electrical cells	▼	Flowerless plants / Australian marsupial	▼	Customary practices
▼		▼				▼		▼
Recede / Immune ▶				Ms Amos, songstress ▶				
▼								
Film props and scenery / For every ▶				Additional / Anger ▶				
▼			Lyricist, Gershwin / Happening ▼				Disputes	
Person held in servitude	Extremely / Young insect ▶		▼			Main artery of the body	▼	Tailed heavenly body
▼	▼				Portion of a circumference ▶	▶		▼
Devoured / Edge ▶				Company badge / Vital ▶				
▼				▼	Peculiar ▶			
Elect / Francisco, US city ▶					Stand for a golf ball ▶			
▼			Raising agent ▶					

Overcame	▼	Cereal crop	▼	Hindu meditation and relaxation method	▼	Capital of the Maldives — Tried out	▼	Wager
▶		▼				▼		Covered with small pieces of rock
Embellish — Impenetrable mist ▶				Allows ▶ Of a kind specified				▼
Rubs out, obliterates ▶				▼			Don	
▶			Roads		Number in a brace ▶		▼	
Admirer		Shield ▶	▼					
▶					Division of a week ▶			
Decease		Incision		Sum up	▼	Identical		Clubs used in the game of cricket
Pigmented spot on the skin	Fertilised plant ovules — Have	▼				▼	Bronzing of the skin caused by the sun	▼
▶	▼			Information ▶			▼	
Preposition — Social insects ▶					Coaster ▶			
▶				Writing implements ▶				

118

115

21st letter of the Greek alphabet	▼	Compound which can turn litmus blue	▼	Daniel ___, Bond actor	Mystic, super-natural	▼	US state between Nevada and Colorado	Common cyst of the skin
Loose woman		▼			▼		Turning into alcohol	▼
►				Informal restaurant	►		▼	
Carni-vorous venomous lizard, ___ monster	Cooking area	►						
►				Book of Psalms		Mr Geller, spoon-bender		Large northern deer
Boast	Rugs	Feather worn as an ornament	▼		▼		▼	
Singer of folk songs, troubadour	▼							
Reflexive pronoun		Cleansing agent	Eagle		Fluid used for writing	►		
►		▼	▼			Actress daughter of Sam Wana-maker		Pin
Put in order	►				Slide fastener	►	▼	
Frolic	Plant also known as the windflower	►						
►					Hen's produce	►		

119

116

Backache	▼	Halo	Existed, lived	▼	Robe	▼	Distribute in small portions	Basic unit of money in Albania
⌐				▼			Really	▼
Called on the phone		Female member of a religious order	Figure out ▶			▼		
⌐		▼	Period of seven consecutive days					
Committee	Forum in ancient Greece		Someone who breaks free	False statement		Turkish commander		Northern deer with very large antlers
⌐	▼		▼	▼	Yes ▶	▼		▼
Compel	Produce tones with the voice ▶						Swiftness	
⌐					Enquire ▶		▼	
Native of northern Scandinavia		Doctor of Philosophy (abbr)		Beds for babies	▼	United Nations agency (inits)		Chemical that carries genetic information (inits)
⌐		▼		Was in debt to ▶		▼		▼
Bare	Infidel, unbeliever ▶							
⌐			Salt of carbonic acid, used in soap powders ▶					

Mimic	▼	Anger	▼	Aquatic creature	Difficult experience	▼	Flat mass of ice floating at sea	That girl
Fuel ►	▼				▼		Limp and soiled as if hauled through mud	▼
►				Loose flowing garment ►			▼	
Crooked	City north of Calgary, Alberta (3,4) ►							
►				Hypothetical remedy for all ills (4-3)		Gaming cube		Work unit
Blemish, indication of damage done	Entreaty		Framework of a military unit	▼		▼		▼
Queer	▼ ►							
Gender that refers to inanimate objects		Encourage	Duck		Ovum ►			
►		▼	▼			Wing of an insect		Seedcase of a pea or bean
Geographical region of indefinite boundary ►					High mountain ►	▼		▼
Brood (on)	Italian astronomer and mathematician ►							
►					Put in ►			

Pathfinder	▼	Shaped like a ring	Destroy completely	▼	Puts into a letterbox	Variety of mandarin orange	▼	Manu-facturer of toy bricks
Engage in drunken merry-making ►	▼		▼			▼		Fit of shivering or shaking
Difficult concern ►					Turkish com-mander ►			▼
Building block ►					Fit out ►			
►					Girl's name	Wash away debris to separate minerals ▼		
Makes senseless by a blow	Fight (3-2)		Harness strap	Fool or hoax	▼			
Malignant tumour, a major type of cancer ►	▼		▼					Area sur-rounding the hole on a golf course
►				Called on the phone ►				▼
Simple		Liable		Opening		Sauce used in Chinese cookery	The day before	
Savoury taste ex-perience ►		▼		▼	Observe ►	▼	▼	
►			Appearing earlier in the same text					
Swab	Faucet ►				Japanese monetary unit ►			

122

Tribe of Arizona, USA	Fiend	Variety of eating apple	▼	Gadget, contraption (coll)	Bedroom on a ship	Give a speech	▼	Bounders, scoundrels
⌐	▼	▼		Fossil fuel ▶	▼	▼		
Muscular pouch in birds, for grinding food ▶								Peppery
Number of turns in 60 seconds (inits) ▶				Wallop ▶				▼
⌐							Shake	
Bank	Borne on the water		Court game	Girl's name	⌐		▼	
⌐	▼		▼	▼	Common amphibian	Con-densed but memorable saying		Bring into play
Father Christmas		Anger ▶				▼		▼
⌐					Alliterative term for a young woman		Browning of the skin caused by the sun	
Errol ___, swash-buckling film star (1909–59)		Invalidate ▶			▼		▼	
⌐				Gelling agent ▶				
Public passenger vehicle	'Night', Christmas carol ▶							

120

Man-eating giant		Roman goddess of agriculture	Secret watcher		Person skilled in a particular type of therapy		Rear-facing point on an arrow	Caustic washing solution
Basic exam level (inits)					Pointed tool			
Fix							Girl's name	
					Fatal disease of cattle (inits)			
Mineral	Number indicated by the Roman XI		Couples		Clair-voyance (inits)	Relating to extent		Morsel left at a meal, crumb
Strong black coffee								
US film actress, ___ Moore		Has in mind		Box				
				Breathe noisily, as when exhausted				
Word that denotes an action					Implores		Be indebted to	Country, capital Washington DC (inits)
Relieve					Notice of intent to pay (inits)			
			Chews on with the teeth					
Small hotel	Call for help (inits)				Field suitable for grazing by livestock			

124

Neither good nor bad (2-2)	Elliptical	Navy man	▼	Multitude	Unsuccessful person	Exceed	▼	Eldest of Bart Simpson's two sisters
◣	▼	▼		Cut of meat taken from the side and back ►		▼		
Assorted ►								Went faster
Be of service ►				Principal actor ►				▼
◣							Unspecified quantity	
Claimed, but not proved	Ancient (3-3)		Contraption	Other than what is under consideration	►		▼	
◣	▼		▼	▼	Horse's coat when sprinkled with white or grey	Stadium		Tip at an angle
Big		Ever ►				▼		▼
◣					Granny		Moody, English actor	
Depends on		Group containing one or more species ►			▼		▼	
◣				By an unknown author, in short ►				
Succulent plant with spikes of showy flowers		One who pays rent ►						

Woman's garment (abbr)	▼	Capable of making a mistake	▼	Eight singers who perform together	Spanish rice dish	▼	Former communist country (inits)	Cheerio
Sum-marises briefly ▶		▼			▼		Occurring at a very favourable time (6-4)	▼
▶				Pale grey ▶			▼	
Heavy open wagon	Official who is expected to ensure fair play	▶						
▶				Act of assistance		Alias (inits)		Epoch
Basic rhythmic unit in a piece of music	Edible fat		Person held in servitude	▼ ▶		▼		▼
One who runs naked through a public place ▶	▼							
Act well or properly		Musical instrument	Figure-skating jump		Mother of the ancient Irish gods ▶			
▶		▼	▼			By means of		Unit of gravi-tational force
Cab ▶					Cabbage, carrots, etc (abbr) ▶	▼		▼
Abundant	Lean back ▶							
▶					Consumed ▶			

123

Former communist country (inits)	South American monkey with a long tail	Moves in a sensuous or stealthy manner	◣	Former French coin	Insensitive or heartless	In the centre of	◣	Open tart
◣				Muscular back part of the leg	◣	◣		
US 'Heart of Dixie' state	◣							Biblical first woman
Family	◣			Solitary	◣			◣
◣							Fall behind	
Cathedral city	Insight-fulness		Children's outdoor toy	Leer	◣		◣	
◣	◣		◣	Short sleep		Paragon		Swellings, protuber-ances
Lowest adult male singing voice		National flag	◣			◣		◣
◣				Acid present in all living cells (inits)			Large monkey	
Roman province at the time of Christ		Counter-pane	◣		◣		◣	
◣				Back of the neck	◣			
Second letter of the Greek alphabet	Very large marine mammals	◣						

124

Cereal thrown at weddings	▼	Highest female voice	Mislay	▼	Liveliness and energy	▼	Open space at the top of a house	Insect such as an ant
Small area of water-surrounded land		▼	▼		One of four playing cards in a deck			▼
Barrel maker	▶						Call forth	
▶				Toilet (coll)	Sleep state in which dreaming occurs (inits)		▼	
Large mush-rooms (Boletus edulis)	Assuage	▶		▼				
Welsh university town	Respira-tory disorder		Brief look		Small measure of drink	▶		
▶	▼		▼			Person afflicted with Hansen's disease		Outmoded
God of the Sun	▶			Having little money	Went first	▶		▼
Powerful herbivore with a horned snout		Part of a church that contains the altar		▼			Source of metal	
▶					Fixture found on a chimney stack	▶	▼	
Writing material		Stick or hold together	▶					
▶					Crimson	▶		

128

125

Effigy	▼	Comical	Rudolf ___, WWII Nazi leader	▼	Insincere talk about religion or morals	Old Testament prophet	▼	Ditch used to divide lands (2-2)
Guru ►	▼	▼				▼		Measure (out)
Expression used at the end of a prayer ►					Electrical resistance unit ►			▼
Blast of wind ►					Means of returning something by post (inits) ►			
⌐				Cowboy film	Shaft on which a wheel rotates		Bronze	
Fewer	Check accounts	Fritter away	▼	▼			▼	
Attach to ►	▼					Take as one's own		Ringworm
⌐		Tilt	►			▼		▼
Domestic parasite	Hollow, flexible structure resembling a bag	'Father ___', TV sitcom	►				Tiny	
Offshore area ►	▼				Be in possession of ►		▼	
⌐		Indian currency unit	►					
Hour at which something is due (inits)	Is able to ►				Afternoon meal ►			

129

Long narrative poem	▼	Cook in an oven	▼	Bowl for baptismal water	▼	___ pole, tribal emblem	▼	Remove clips, as from a washing line
Deep ▶	▼							
Electrically charged particle ▶				Bathroom fixtures		Firearm		Swinging or sliding barriers
▶				▼		▼		
Dispersed	Pose		Mexican comrade ▶					
Dance move ▶	▼				Burden of responsibility		For a short time	
Poke or thrust abruptly		Bright blue	Of the Sun ▶		▼		▼	
▶	▼			Tidings ▶				
Wooing	Frequently (poetically)		Went faster	Expression of disapproval		Fodder		Animal's foot
▶	▼		▼	▼		▼		▼
German woman ▶					Wing of an insect ▶			
Marquee ▶					Coniferous tree ▶			

127

Star which ejects material	Carry out	Blank	▾	Craftsman who works with stone	Articles of commerce	Cowboy contest	▾	Change direction
▾	▾	▾		Developed ▸	▾	▾		
Double-reed instrument ▸								Pose
Umberto ___, 'The Name of the Rose' author ▸				___ and ends ▸				▾
▸							Cereal grass	
Extremely poisonous substance	Beat through cleverness		Cord hole	Act presumptuously ▸			▾	
▸	▾		▾	▾	Smut from a fire	Tract of level wasteland		Grows from, originates
Made a written record of		Sailing vessels ▸				▾		▾
▸					Joke		Brandy measure	
Gas formerly used as an anaesthetic		Official emissary ▸			▾		▾	
▸				Particle ▸				
Money extracted as a penalty		Garment worn on the lower half of the body ▸						

Meat-based delicacy (5,7)		Adult male person		Chooses		Spoken		Blasphemed
One who is playfully mischievous				Defeat in battle				
Large open vessel for liquids				Sicilian volcano		Fill with optimism		Portly
Not marked by the use of reason		Club-shaped object used in bowling	Location of a building		Give permission to			
Bridge					Rapid bustling commotion			
Verdi opera with an Egyptian theme					Lone Star State of the USA		Oil-bearing laminated rock	
				Examination				
Reserve of money		Wheat-like cereal plant				Number of turns in 60 seconds (inits)		Coniferous tree
Chopping tool				Medical 'photograph' (1-3)				
Lairs		Metal paper fastener						
				Fish-eating diving duck				

129

Loud-speaker system	▼	Take in with the tongue (3-2)	▼	Popular carbonated drink	▼	Brief swim	▼	Asian spice
►				▼				
Character-ised by lust ——— Abrogate		Explode with a bang	►			Measure of land		Appeal
►				Electric current unit (abbr) ——— Boorish	► ▼			▼
Athletic facility		Package ——— Adult female horses	►					
►		▼	Withdraw from an organisa-tion	Compulsion ——— Hardened to	►			
Calm, with no emotional agitation	Digression	►	▼				Noisy riotous fight	
►						Com-ponent	▼	'Children in ___', annual BBC appeal
Light-beam amplifier	Old French gold or silver coin ——— Assist	►			Female swan	► ▼		▼
►	▼				General name for beer	►		
Contri-buted		Extent	►					
►					Diminutive of Edward	►		

130

Capital of Cambodia (5,4)	▼	Cut the wool from	▼	Book-length story	Tidings	▼	Nautical term used in hailing	▼
⌐								
Disliking being photographed (6-3)		Jumble		Sharp tap	Group of countries in a special alliance		Dog-like nocturnal mammal	
⌐	▼		▼		▼		▼	
Make less tight ►						Root vegetable		Portion
Donkey	County		Tubes ►			▼		▼
⌐	▼		Pretend	Mentally healthy ►				
Steals (coll)		Large luxurious car (abbr)	▼	Mediocre and disdained writer	Piece of scrap material	►		
⌐		▼		▼			Time period	
Girl's name ►					Named prior to marriage ►		▼	
►			Mound of stones piled up as a memorial					
Precious or semi-precious stone	Producer of acorns ►				Tap lightly ►			

Therefore	▼	Avid	Period of time	▼	Explosions	▼	Back part of a shoe	Fixed
Bobbin ▶		▼	▼		Units (1/6 inch) used in printing ▶			▼
Out-building for housing a car ▶							Fertile desert areas	
▶					Biblical character whose wife was turned into salt ▶		▼	
Roman cloaks	Produce incisors, molars, etc		Consumed		Domestic swine	Device for connecting plugs and sockets		Plant juice
Enter unlawfully onto someone's property	▼		▼		▼	▼		▼
Financial obligation		Muscle	Approxi-mation of quantity, degree or worth ▶					
▶		▼	Short intake of breath ▶					
Wood plant ▶			▼	Catch sight of			Good discern-ment	Venomous snake
Christian Andersen, storyteller ▶				Popular beverage ▶			▼	▼
▶			Gambits ▶					
Evergreen tree	Word indicating a negative answer ▶			Fabric with prominent rounded crosswise ribs ▶				

King of beasts	▼	Awful	▼	Irish republic	▼	Causes psychological suffering	▼	Traditional panto tale, '___ in the Wood'
Unfriendly ▶	▼							
Device used to propel a boat ▶			Informal farewell remark (2-2)		Boundary			Yield to another's wish or opinion
◤			▼		▼			
Still in doubt	Division of an ocean		Come up ▶					
Arrangement ▶	▼						Dreadfully	
Foundation		Oil-bearing laminated rock	Away ▶				▼	
◣		▼	Agitate ▶					
One who plays practical jokes on others	Common type of rodent		Neither	Range of knowledge		Father ___, TV sitcom		'The Catcher in the ___', Salinger novel
◣	▼		▼	▼		▼		▼
Succulent plant with spikes of showy flowers ▶				Cambridgeshire cathedral city ▶				
Small slender gull with a forked tail ▶				Colourant ▶				

133

Concerning someone's private life		Chimney-pot cover		Doves' home		Loaned / Countrified		Place to exercise
								Loose-fitting
Process of getting better / Bunkum				Dull / Distant in space or time				
Perspires							At another time	
			Relatively fast warship		Label			
Pass between mountain peaks		Housing or outer covering						
					Affectedly modest			
Bear, convey		Detest		Liveliness and energy		Alone		Part of the ear
Exclamation expressive of sorrow	Homes for bees / Be prostrate						Prune	
				Game played on horseback				
Article / Aristocrat					Tennis stroke			
				Manage, make do				

134

Drink often mixed with alcohol	Portent	Moved to music	▼	Adult male voice	Prefix denoting a partly British connection	Pleasantly cold and invigorating	▼	Devices that fit locks
▼	▼	▼		In golf, played a hole in one stroke	▼	▼		
Brickwork ▶								Bronze
Printing measures				Essence ▶				▼
▶							___ de Cologne, perfume	
Disentangles	Incapable		Appear	Uncommon	▶		▼	
▶	▼		▼	▼	Blatant	Existing		College administrators
More ill-mannered		Rove in search of booty ▶				▼		▼
▶					Informal name for a sailor		Abbreviation for the word 'numbers'	
Long-legged waterbird		Light-sensitive membrane ▶			▼		▼	
▶				Bath's river ▶				
Shared on-line journal		Departure ▶						

138

Carry	▼	Humble	▼	Laugh loudly and harshly	Less smart	Large nation (inits)	Hoop that covers a wheel	▼
Organ of hearing	►		▼	At the proper time	►	▼		
Calcu-lating machine	►						Bulgarian monetary unit	
►				Composed of men or boys	►		▼	
Address God, usually with a plea	Unfore-seen difficulty		Discharge	Insensitive or heartless		Not in good health		Come to a halt
Become conscious of	▼		▼	▼		▼		▼
Coral reef		British nobleman	►				Concur	
►					Chap	►	▼	
Former Portu-guese province in China		Large northern deer	►			Work unit	~	Centre of a storm
►					Before, poetically	▼		▼
State of depression		County in southern England	►					
►					Word of surprise	►		

Capable of being handled, touched or felt	Quantity of paper equal to 500 sheets	Speck of soot	Hindu garment / Country of Moscow		Uneven
					Compere (coll)
Agricultural area / Moldovan money unit		Boorish / Exclude			
Regional dialect				Primitive chlorophyll-containing organism	
	By unspecified means	Hollow, flexible structure resembling a bag			
Thrash hard	Comparative figure of speech				
		Grow old			
Distribute	Pigmented spot on the skin	US government unit (inits)	Burrowing bivalve mollusc		Propelled with the feet
Winnie-the-___, A A Milne's famous bear	Army doctor / Scull			___ Lanka, country formerly known as Ceylon	
		Too, as well			
Much (1,3) / Prepare by infusion		Unit of surface area equal to 100 sq metres			
		Among			

137

Enquire	▼	Laugh nervously	▼	Priest	Medical building	▼	Front part of the human leg below the knee
							Mature female deer
Apply stiffening agent to cloth	▼			▼			Extent
						▼	
►			Swimming pool ►				
Slide	Apprentice ►						
►			Amber-coloured dessert wine		Archaic form of the word 'your'		Pop duo formed by Andy Bell and Vince Clarke
Gambling stake	Support	Head-dress worn by a bishop ►	▼		▼		▼
One who gives a sermon	▼						
Melt	Salty Greek cheese	Long arduous journey	Old-fashioned affirmative answer ►				
►	▼	▼		White lie	Robert E ___, general in the US Civil War		
Persian fairy ►			Feverish cold (abbr) ►	▼	▼		
Port city of Japan	Type of dog ►						
►				Four-winged insect ►			

141

138

Produce milk for a baby to drink	▼	Go out with	Arouse from slumber	▼	Con-servative	▼	Gather, as of crops	Rug
◣					▼		Run easily	▼
Container with a perforated lid used at table		Food in a pastry shell	Australian marsupial ▶				▼	
◣		▼						
Last letter of the Greek alphabet	Fine Burgundy wine usually white		Entrance	Painting, sculpture, etc		Conces-sion given to mollify		Assis-tance
◣	▼		▼	▼	Large body of water ▶	▼		▼
Antarctic explorer		Bow for a stringed instrument ▶					Frequently	
◣				Seedcase ▶		▼		
Chew on with the teeth		Mimic		Brewery cart	▼	Egg cells		Noah's boat
◣		▼		Roster ▶		▼		▼
Animal hunted for food	Tedious business ▶							
◣			Pull with a sudden movement ▶					

139

Deficient in quantity compared with demand	▼	That man	▼	Audacious	Jelly based on fish or meat stock	▼	Bird associated with the Tower of London	▼
Compelling attractiveness or charm ►	▼							
Atmosphere ⎯ Truce				Afternoon nap	Informal farewell remark (2-2)		Metropolis	
◣				▼	▼		▼	
Account book	Nicotinic acid ► ⎯ Type of fish trap							
◣		▼				One score and ten		Washed off soap
Clumsy	Island republic in the South Pacific Ocean		Forest god ⎯ Machine used for printing			▼		▼
◣	▼		▼		Memorisation by repetition		Adept	
Agricultural ► ⎯ Hill of sand					▼		▼	
◣				Spheres ►				
Move to a different place ► ⎯ Hard fruits								
◣				Looked at ►				

143

140

Cyclone	▼	Roster	Artificial covering for a tooth	▼	Become evident to the mind	▼	District	Hard durable wood
◣					▼		Prefix meaning 'half'	▼
Grassy garden area		United Nations agency (inits)	Bamboo-eating mammal	▶				
◣		▼		Period of seven consecutive days				
Large ladle	Cut thinly		Supervise	Small seed		Last letter of the alphabet		Coin, a division of a Burmese kyat
◣	▼		▼	▼	Slide fastener	▶	▼	▼
Grovel		Moral weakness	▶				Made a written record of	
◣					Chemical that carries genetic information (inits)	▶	▼	
Professional charges		Fairy		Two considered together	▼	Archaic form of the word 'your'		Mineral
◣		▼		Germanic name	▶	▼		▼
Free from danger	Animal skin	▶						
◣			Park in central London	▶				

141

For what reason?	▼	Make attractive or lovable	▼	Imposed a levy	Mammals of the weasel family	▼	Lock openers	All the same
Vehicle for carrying a coffin ▶		▼			▼		Fruit also called the Chinese gooseberry	▼
▶				Uncouth ill-bred person ▶			▼	
Short-tailed wildcat	Down payment ▶							
▶				Add sugar		Across or above, poetically		Rechewed food
Unwanted plant	Divulge confidential information (coll)		Unemotional person ▶	▼		▼		▼
Look around a shop randomly	▼						Angry	
Gentle teasing		'Children in ___', annual BBC appeal	Story		Free ▶		▼	
▶		▼	▼			Branch of the British armed forces (inits)		Evergreen tree
Drum, pound ▶				Column of light ▶				▼
Burdened	Bring up ▶							
▶				Not many ▶				

145

Cancelled		Creative person		Flat masses of ice floating at sea		Of the most excellent quality	Pâté made from goose liver (4,4)	
High male singing voice								
				Woody part of plants		Higher in position	Regret	
Rounded thickly curled hairdo	Consis-tency							
					Breed of dog originating in Asia			
Lawn flower	Given special treatment to aid in recovery	Sufferer from Hansen's disease						
		Pigment prepared from cuttlefish ink			Each and every		High male singing voice	
Insect		Stings						
				Un-matched		Reverence		Female deer
Soft creamy French cheese	Country, capital Warsaw							
					Court			
Offensively mal-odorous		Stick						

143

Formerly	Close by	Cursory	▼	Work-stations	Profit	Got up	▼	Organs of locomotion and balance in fishes
⌐	▼	▼		Food used in a trap ▶		▼		
From the Orient ▶								Consume food
Seek an answer to ▶				Olfactory organ ▶				▼
⌐							Strong washing solution	
Compresses with violence	One of a kind		Locations	Fabric of compressed matted fibres ▶			▼	
⌐	▼		▼	Every one		Coach		Relaxes
Soft moist part of a fruit		Last thing mentioned ▶		▼		▼		▼
⌐					Long period of time		Move the head up and down	
Concluding		Removes filth ▶		▼		▼		
⌐				Uproar ▶				
Certain		Rises to one's feet ▶						

147

Total admission receipts at a sports event	Declare formally as true	Chinese philosophy based on Lao-tzu's writings	▼	Reddish-brown dye used mostly on the hair	Ailment	Haemor-rhage	▼	Head of the chapter of a cathedral
⌐	▼	▼		Mountain goat ►	▼	▼		
Popular flavour of ice cream ►								Golf peg
Long period of time ►				Time from Ash Wednesday to Holy Saturday ►				▼
⌐							Large African antelope	
Girl's name	Fit for cultivation		Deter-mined in advance	Rim, brink ►			▼	
⌐	▼		▼	Clair-voyance (inits)		About		Outcome
Source of illu-mination		Deli-verance ►		▼	▼			▼
⌐					Tune		Male child	
Shows concern		Not dense ►			▼		▼	
⌐				Religious painting ►				
Sticky paste		Despot ►						

148

Knead	▼	Frozen rain	Resin-like substance secreted by certain insects	▼	Decent	▼	Edible leguminous seed	Belonging to him
◣					▼		Ballet dancer's skirt	▼
Pincer		Alias (inits)	American raccoon	◤		◞	▼	
◣	▼		Responsibility	◤				
Fastener	Ocean-going vessel		Painted structures of a stage set	Put a snooker ball down a hole		Small vegetable		Edgar Allan ___, US writer and poet
◣	▼		▼	▼	Young seal	◤ ▼		▼
Bay or cove		Doves' home	◤			Irritates, annoys		
◣					(They) exist	◤ ▼		
Scottish hillside		Had a meal		Strip of fried potato	◤ ▼	Compass point at 67.5 degrees (inits)		Tolstoy, Russian writer
◣		▼		The Underworld	◤	▼		▼
Australian term for a young kangaroo	Cadet	◤						
◣				Basic monetary unit of the Philippines	◤			

146

Fully developed	Know-ledge (abbr)	Unnatural lack of colour in the skin	▼	East African country	Faint-hearted	Liquorice-flavoured seeds	▼	Excavates
⌐	▼	▼		Part of an animal ►	▼	▼		
Former capital of China ►								Small insecti-vorous bird
Two-winged insect ►				Cloud ►				▼
⌐							Show dis-pleasure vocally	
North Star	Smear with ointment		Female germ cells of a plant	Volcano in New Guinea	⌐		▼	
⌐	▼		▼	▼	Obligation to pay or do something	English novelist		Young bird of prey
Tree with pods used as a chocolate substitute		Religious cult practised in the Caribbean ►				▼		▼
⌐					For what reason?		Increases	
Magnate		Legal ►			▼		▼	
⌐				Expect and wish ►				
Leg joint		Most timid ►						

150

Beer		Become famous		Disclosed or revealed		Girdle	Block of flats	
Worthy of high praise								
				Patty Bouvier's twin sister in 'The Simpsons'		Capacious	Fluid product of an inflammation	
Irreverent, saucy	Form differently							
					Mother			
Endure	One who leaves to live abroad		Fall out of date					
			Hire		Expression of disapproval		Fume	
Social insect		Most recent						
				Country, capital Washington DC (inits)		Diminutive of Henry		Informer
Bake in a kiln so as to harden		Writer						
					Alias (inits)			
Alloy of copper and zinc		Young bird of prey						

148

No longer new, un-interesting ▼	▼	Alloy of mercury with another metal	Pool	▼	Motorcycle	Bear a young cow	▼	Portuguese city in the Algarve
Milk-pudding ingredient ▶		▼				▼		Fool, idiot (coll)
In a murderous frenzy ▶					Prowess ▶			▼
Country road ▶					Depressed ▶			
▶				Fowl that frequents coastal waters	Misplace		Earlier in time than, poetically	
Had in one's hands	Tiny morsel of bread or cake		Mixture of rain and snow ▶	▼	▼		▼	
Raised medallion ▶	▼					Endure, put up with		Nominal
▶			Valuable quality ▶			▼		▼
Provide with weapons		Economic assistance	Stake ▶				Take advantage of	
Land-locked republic in north-west Africa ▶		▼			Diving bird of northern seas ▶		▼	
▶			Use water to remove soap ▶					
US law enforcement agency (inits)	Informal term for a father	▶			Lair ▶			

152

149

Full of rancour	Brain-teaser	Of sound mind	▼	Retained	▼	Highest volcano in Europe	▼	Motor coaches
▼	▼	▼						
Forty winks ▶			'The Catcher in the ___', Salinger novel		Connec-ted with birth			Chucked
Restricted computer network ▶			▼			▼		▼
▼			Make a new request to be sup-plied with	Deciduous tree ▶				
Grow old	Forcibly pulled apart	▼					Gambling establish-ment	
▼			Con-sumption	Expert ▶			▼	
Bundle of hay or straw	Crack in a lip caused usually by cold	Declare illegal ▶	▼					
▼					Make an incision	Biblical man		Bronze
Marks left by old wounds		Dis-honesty ▶			▼	▼		▼
▼			Arm bone ▶					
False		Fixed portion that is allotted ▶						

153

Was dressed in	▼	The Flint- stones' home town	Aye / River of York	▼	Bad luck	▼	Mariners	▼
Double- reed woodwind instrument ►		▼	▼		Wrath ►			
Employs again ►							Conduct	
►				Without blemish	Yearly assembly of share- holders (inits) ►		▼	
Marries	Remain- der ►		▼					
Bullied, intimi- dated	Former monetary unit of Portugal		Paper handker- chief		French word for 'wine' ►			
►	▼		▼					Additional
Short theatrical episode ►					Named prior to marriage ►			▼
Evil spell		Recep- tacle for a coin ►					Allow	
►					In the month preceding this one (abbr) ►		▼	
Rec- tangular containers		Loan shark ►						
►					Hour at which something is due (inits) ►			

154

151

Be against / Science of vision and eye-care	▼	Gawped / Cardinal number	▼	Collision that is narrowly avoided (4,4)	▼	Colour / Forest plants	▼	Scene of the Allied conference in 1945
◣	▼					▼		▼
Pin / Long and slippery fish (6,3)	▶			Expanse / Alleviate	▶			
◣				▼				
Goddess of retribution		Express grief / Small arachnids	▶				One who takes spoils or plunder (as in war)	
◣		▼					▼	
Morsel	"Beware the ___ of March" / Dramatist	▶		–		Girl's name		River which flows through Kelso
◣	▼		Disorderly outburst or tumult (2-2)	Native of Edinburgh, eg. / Expert	▶	▼		▼
Greek letter / Relate	▶		▼	▼	Depleted / Extremely cold	▶		
◣					▼			
Gen (abbr)		Edict	▶					
◣				Back garden	▶			

155

More favourable position	▼	Perfect	▼	Harbour	Contributed	▼	Series of waves in the hair	▼
◣								
Ray of high-intensity radiation (5,4)		Part of a window-frame		Traditional Jewish courtesy title for a man	Little terror		Woman's dress style with a flared skirt (1-4)	
◣		▼		▼	▼		▼	
Covering that protects an inside surface	▶					Support oneself		Portion
Unit of length equal to 45 inches	Ruminant mammal		Foundation	▶		▼		▼
◣	▼		Section of a play	Succession of notes forming a sequence	▶			
Cattle farms		Short letter	▼	Leading man	Implore	▶		
◣		▼		▼			___ de Janeiro, Brazilian port	
Small particle of dust	▶				Wrath	▶	▼	
◣			Plant exudation	▶				
___ King Cole, jazz pianist and singer	Self-importance	▶			Toddler	▶		

Position of professor	Molten rock	▼	Excite-ment	▼	Uttering words	▼	Go in / Punk rocker, Adam ___	▼
⌐					Metal cooking vessel	►	▼	
Assertion	Falsehood		Broker / Of a thing	►				
⌐	▼		▼		Took in solid food / Glide over snow	►		
Minus		Duty / Article of clothing	►				Light mid-afternoon meal	
⌐		▼		Equip-ment / Pare	►		▼	Travels very quickly
Domestic birds	Wipe off		Longs for / Cook slowly in liquid	▼				▼
⌐	▼		▼		Empty space / Blow	►		
Assigns a rank to / Celestial body	►					Frost	Can	
⌐						▼	▼	
Stitch / That woman	►			Bitter	►			
⌐			Affords access to	►				

157

154

Enter (4,2) / Motor vessel		Gem / Known globally (5,6)		Desert, leave		Hack-neyed / Aromatic, edible bulb		Bill for an amount due
Cut (the grass, for example)				'Karenina', novel by Leo Tolstoy				
Plant of many seasons / Sick				Child's toy / Drink with a spoon				
			Boy / Poplar				Amount of time	
Bring to a close / Clench, clutch	Mythical being / Spanish wine					Careless speed		Gives notice of impending danger
					Chop with an axe			
Pixie / Sticky, tacky				Soldier (abbr) / Japanese coin				
					Form of address to a man			
Summer month / Existed, lived					2240 pounds			
			Demands					

158

155

Old-fashioned		Rise from a sitting position (5,2)	Milk pudding ingredient		Heal	American ___, poisonous shrub		Approximation of quantity, degree or worth
Adopted in order to deceive								Having a strong healthy body
Heavenly body					Meadow			
Aromatic grey-green herb					Light touch or stroke			
				Projection behind and above a horse's hoof	Collection of miscellaneous things		Word of surprise	
Game also known as bingo	Last letter of the Greek alphabet		Blacksmith's workplace					
Blackbird						In the area		Authoritative declaration (3-2)
			Slates					
Unit of electric current		Strong anger	Toilet (coll)				Source of metal	
Banking system					Affecting shyness			
			Scorches					
Period of conflict	Northern deer with very large antlers				Sign of the zodiac			

156

Addition that extends a main building	▼	To the full extent (poetically)	▼	Repeats the words of another	Ringworm	▼	Climbing plant supporter	▼
Particle with zero mass when at rest ▶	▼							
Prefix meaning 'recent' ▶ / Insect			Glacial episode in the past (3,3)	Humble request for help		Singer (albums include 'Life for Rent')	
▼			▼	▼		▼	
Tenant	Cream-filled pastry / Conjecture ▶						
▼	▼				Precipitated		Conformity with some aesthetic standard of propriety
Small branch	More lacking in colour	Biblical character / Contribution ▶			▼		
▼	▼	▼		Expressed in words		Former coin of India and a girl's name	
Loss of memory sufferer ▶ / Prune				▼			
▼			Last Stuart monarch, Queen of England ▶				
Extremely hungry ▶ / Be anxious							
▼			Name given to 6 June 1944 (1-3) ▶				

157

Having curative properties	Fertilised egg	Two singers who perform together	▼	Pear-shaped yellowish or purple fruits	▼	Prescribed selection of foods	▼	Desert animal
L	▼	▼						
Drinking vessel ▶				Be in debt		Appre-ciation		Cause to lose courage
Infatuated ▶				▼		▼		▼
▶			Cautious		Wing of an insect ▶			
Morsel left at a meal, crumb	Large brown fungi (Boletus edulis) ▶	▼				Dissimilar		
▶				Umberto ___, 'The Name of the Rose'	Large cask for beer or wine ▶		▼	
Spanish artist (1746–1828)	Supreme god of ancient Greek mythology	Feel contrition ▶		▼				
▶					Boy child	Distres-sing		Hallucino-genic drug (inits)
Ancient Mexican civilisation	Palaeonto-logical relic ▶			▼	▼		▼	
▶				Acorn-producing trees ▶				
Eastern teacher	Alighted ▶							

158

US space-flight agency (inits)	Word said at the end of a prayer	Highly seasoned fatty sausage	▼	Faux pas	Theme	Commonly encountered	▼	Expression of incredulity (2,2)
▶	▼	▼		Soft or soggy mass ▶	▼	▼		
Cosa Nostra members ▶								Charge a contribution to state revenue ▼
Imp ▶				Tussock ▶				
▶							Pointed tool	
Deficiency of red blood cells	Place where something begins		Surgical knife	Reverse an action	▶		▼	
▶	▼		▼	▼	Fibre which is woven into linen	Solitary		Of questionable taste or morality
Thick stew made of rice and chicken		Chronological records ▶				▼		▼
▶					State in which dreaming occurs (inits)		Nothing	
Demon	Outermost region of the sun's atmosphere ▶				▼		▼	
▶				First name of authoress Blyton ▶				
Presidential assistant	At an opportune moment ▶							

159

Showy and festive party	Throb dully	Musée du ___, principal museum of France		Skin disease affecting domestic animals	Grave	Au revoir		Home-work
				Hindu woman's garment				
Acknow-ledge defeat								Note in the tonic sol-fah scale
Embrace				Tears violently				
							Make the sound of a dove	
Daydream	Sickener		Mythical monster said to live in swamps	Expres-sion of pain				
				Popular vegetable		Unusually energetic		Volatile liquid used to thin paint (abbr)
The BBC, collo-quially		Outcome						
					Coin, a division of a Burmese kyat		Old cloth measure	
Pasta in short tubes with diagonally cut ends		Small, noisy dog						
				Bark in a high-pitched tone				
Group of islands, capital Suva		Beads produced by oysters						

British peer	Against	Shows a response	▼	Highest peak in the Alps, Mont ___	Seat behind the rider of a motorbike	Coupling	▼	Units of work or energy
◣	▼	▼		Without blemish or contamination	►	▼		
Drawing close	►							Burned remains
Prepare leather	►			Eldest of Bart Simpson's two sisters	►			▼
►							Greek letter	
Small flute	Mass of snow permanently covering the land		Maltreater	Advance slowly	►		▼	
►	▼		▼	Exclamation expressing disgust		Alpine vocal call		Man-handled
Endorsement made in a passport		Mythical monster said to live in watery places ►				▼		▼
►					Profound emotion inspired by a deity		Source of metal	
Correct computer program faults		Trace	►		▼		▼	
►				Had existence	►			
Alleviate		Lurched	►					

Arrowword puzzle 161

Ban / Take exception to		Make-up used on the eyelashes	___ Lanka / Waste product		Appliance for storing food at low temperatures		Sweet-talked
				Consciousness of one's own identity			
Government tax on imports or exports						Avoid	
			Land and the buildings on it	King			
Give medicine to	Confined, imprisoned						
Weighed down	Referee		Redirect		Wander aimlessly in search of pleasure		
							Motorised bicycle
Cause injury				Sleep state in which dreaming occurs (inits)			
Court game resembling handball		Endorsement made in a passport				___ Maria, prayer to the Virgin Mary	
				Bathroom fixture			
Gains victory over		Take away					
				Colour			

Live-action film about a piglet		Measure of gold's purity	Annoying		Flurry	From Holland		Notion
Caustic					Banned insecticide (inits)			
Style of ornamentation in art and architecture								Point
				Putting on clothes	Small amount			
Throw or toss with a quick motion	Early form of sonar used to detect subs						Curve	
					Headgear			
Engine	Stagger, lurch	Force of workers available				Heavenly being		Make a weak, chirping sound
					Represent			
Zodiacal constellation		Vat	Immoral act				Umberto ___, author of 'Foucault's Pendulum'	
Small case for holding sewing articles					Word of surprise			
			Kinswoman					
Highly contagious viral disease (abbr)	Appropriate, seize				Plenty			

166

163

Cause the ruin or downfall of	▼	Part of a rock formation	Honey-producer ——— Three-some	▼	Lacking social graces	▼	Small stream	▼
Brief written record ►		▼	▼		Artificial language, a simplification of Esperanto ►			
Compul-sory force or threat ►							Church passage	
►				Woman's loose dressing gown	Motor vehicle ►		▼	
Lesotho monetary unit	Take in marriage ►			▼				
Woman who dances in a chorus line	Fairground game of ring throwing		Showing a decrease in size or extent		Purpose ►			
►	▼		▼					Lay out in a line
Opaque gem ►					Popular beverage ►			▼
Branchlet		Resort on the French Riviera ►					High mountain	
►					Implement used to propel or steer a boat ►		▼	
Emblem		Immense cloud of gas and dust in space ►						
►					Engage in espionage ►			

Become smaller / Item of furniture	▼	Dearest, darling	For every / Pet form of Louise	▼	▼	Pilot house of a warship (7,5)	▼	▼	Stop thinking about	▼
◤		▼	▼			Yoko ___, John Lennon's widow ►				
Nerve cell ►									Farewell	
◤				Guar-dianship		Henpeck ►		▼		
Deep hole or shaft dug to obtain water	External ►			▼						
Social standing	Capital of Saudi Arabia		Inclines			Egg of a louse ►				
◤	▼		▼							Adult male voice
Eric ___, Monty Python team member ►						Large open vessel ►				▼
Port and resort on the west coast of Florida		Stew ►							Anti-tobacco organi-sation (inits)	
◤						Had existence ►		▼		
Go after with the intent to catch		Emer-gence ►								
◤						17th letter of the Greek alphabet ►				

165

Lowest female singing voice	▼	Fleshy pendulous part of the hearing organ	Snake / Number, the Roman IX	▼	Partnership designed to share risk (5,7)	▼	Furious (3-3) ▼
Transparent optical device	▼	▼			Be in debt ►		
Capital of Taiwan ►						Particular items	
			Artist who carves in stone	Unspecified member of a large series	►	▼	
Cereal crop	African country, formerly Basutoland ►			▼			
Contains or includes	Optimistic	Seed often used on bread rolls		Animal doctor ►			
⌐ ▼		▼					Wipe off
Rind ►				Named prior to marriage ►			▼
Disturb, especially by minor irritations (3,2)		Location ►				Serious offence	
⌐				Country (inits) ►		▼	
Medium once supposed to fill all space		___ dancers, (associated with May Day) ►					
⌐				Compass point at 67.5 degrees (inits) ►			

169

Filled tortilla	▼	'Key ___', 1948 film	▼	Adept	Express opposition	Container for ashes	Car suitable for travelling over rough terrain	▼
Close-sleeved vestment worn by priests ▶		▼		Dominate ▶	▼	▼		
Visitor ▶							Hostel	
▶				Clip at ▶			▼	
Small opening in the skin	Fried piece of food in batter		Cases used to carry belongings	Protective cover for a leg joint (4,3)		Exclamation of surprise		Hydrogen, for example
Traditional ballad (4,4) ▶	▼		▼	▼		▼		▼
Where the sides of a ship curve in to form the bottom	Old word meaning 'in the direction of'		▶				Oarsman	
▶					Periods of 60 minutes (abbr) ▶		▼	
Beat with a piece of leather	Precious or semi-precious stone	▶				Bustle		Earlier in time than, poetically
▶					Over-whelming feeling of wonder ▶	▼		▼
Carrying weapons	Male goose ▶							
▶					Metal-bearing mineral ▶			

167

Inlet / Succeed in a big way (2,3)	▼	Bride-to-be	Crumb / Highest level attainable	▼	Process in the production of alcohol	▼	Entices, lures	▼
		▼	▼		The day before	►		
Combatant who is able to defeat rivals	►						Pined	
				Fortified place where troops are stationed	Chart	►	▼	
Quantity of paper	Disuse	►		▼				
Find repugnant	Sugar extracted from wood or straw		Feeling concern or interest		British system of medical care (inits)	►		
	▼		▼					Senior member of a group
Annum	►				Append	►		▼
Mr Karloff's first name		Narrow fissure in rock	►				French vineyard or group of vineyards	
					Extremely cold	►	▼	
Make a pretence of		Never again (2,4)	►					
					Holy sister	►		

168

Animal associated with the star sign Taurus	___ Major, the Great Bear constellation	Stan ___, film partner of Oliver Hardy	▼	Sore often found in the mouth	Spectacles worn to protect the eyes	Ardent male lover	▼	Tunny fish
◣	▼	▼		Wormlike larva of certain beetles ◤	▼	▼		
Nocturnal mammal native to North America ◤								Granny
Institute legal proceedings against ◤				Agent of the USA's FBI (1-3) ◤			▼	
◣							Affirmative word	
Bombardment	Set down cargo		Bosom	Advance ◤			▼	
◣	▼		▼	Increases		Lustre		Moth-eaten
Swollen underground stem of a daffodil	Brown with a reddish tinge ◤		▼		▼		▼	
◣					Her		Rodent	
High-pitched signal	Claim ◤			▼		▼		
◣				Make warm ◤				
Celebration of the Eucharist	Number denoting a score ◤							

172

Not anti!	⬛	Dan-gerous	⬛	Public dance hall	Involve	⬛	Entrance passage into a mine	At all times, poetically
Bankrupt ▶		⬛			⬛		100th anni-versary	⬛
▶				Pleasant ▶			⬛	
Weight units of 2240 lbs	Disperse ▶							
▶				Decorative under-sheet on a bed		Girl's name		Sum up
Informal greeting	Poorly lit		Prospect ▶	⬛		⬛		⬛
Reduced in worth or impor-tance	⬛							
Child who has lost both parents		Gaze intently	Make warm		Terminate ▶			
▶		⬛	⬛			Former US airline 1930-2001 (inits)		Pain or discomfort
Incisive ▶				Game in which one child chases the others	⬛		⬛	
Rich cake	Type of bet for a win and a place (4,3) ▶							
▶				High mountain ▶				

170

Soporific drug in the form of a tablet (8,4)		High-pitched bark		Diminutive of Elizabeth		Tangerine/grapefruit hybrid		Salted roe of a sturgeon
Caustic washing solution				Cogwheel				
Consume				Common rodents		Slang for 'drunk'		Breathe noisily during sleep
Inflammation of the kidneys		Wooden pin pushed or driven into a surface	Believe to be true		Boy's name			
The present month (abbr)					For			
Common sense, intellect					Consecrate		Burglar	
				Computer memory unit				
Ova		Buddy				21st letter of the Greek alphabet		Abbreviation for hundred-weight
Coat a cake with sugar				Heroic				
Blemish		Kidney-shaped nut						
				Filter				

174

171

Governor	Fertilised egg	Person's manner of walking, pace	▼	Stopper	▼	Money	▼	Asian peninsula
◣		▼						
Adult male person ▶			Be victorious		End in a particular way			City in east-central France on the Rhone
Fairground ride (3,5) ▶			▼		▼			▼
◣			Attack, set on		Word indicating a negative answer ▶			
Painting, sculpture, etc		Social insects	▼				African country of which Kigali is the capital	
◣				Swindle	Large pot for making coffee or tea ▶		▼	
Bends the body as a sign of reverence	Gentle utterance for calling a person's attention	Fasteners with threaded shanks ▶	▼					
◣	▼				And nothing more	Sin		Explosion that fails to occur
Former Portuguese province in China		Straighten up ▶			▼	▼		▼
◣			Official literary language of Pakistan ▶					
Hollow metal device which rings		Group of four ▶						

175

172

Court	▼	Rant	▼	Cloth woven from flax	Set of steps	▼	Flesh used as food	Also
Disinclined to work or exertion ►	▼				▼		One who studies or investigates a subject ▼	▼
⌐				Mountain lake ►				
Become a member	Connected ►							
⌐				Land	Continuing in the same way (abbr) ▼			Cunning
Intend to express or convey	Pastry dishes		Forest plants ►	▼		▼		▼
Support for a statue ►	▼							
Middle		Yule	Hoop that covers a wheel	Utter a shrill loud sound ►				
∟		▼	▼		Small crumb of bread or cake ▼			Might, possibly
Asian plant cultivated for its oily beans ►				Unit of electrical resistance ►	▼		▼	
Mythological beauty, __ of Troy	Former province of northern Ethiopia ►							
∟				Attempt ►				

176

Vagrant	▼	Plunder	Harvest	▼	Appro-priate, seize	▼	French sweet black-currant liqueur	In a laconic manner
Killer whale ▶	▼	▼			Put in ▶			▼
Long, flat-bottomed canal boats ▶							Machine tool	
▶				Bladed chopping tool	Artful ▶		▼	
Thing that must not be done, said, etc (coll) (2-2)	Relating to extent ▶			▼				
Lancashire town that gave its name to a cake	Coarse cloth		Most recent		Pigs' home ▶			
▶	▼		▼			Apprecia-tion		Poker stakes
Alias (inits) ▶				Difficult concern	Light mid-afternoon meal ▶	▼		▼
Donated	Roman cloak ▶		▼				Deciduous tree	
▶					Division of a tennis match ▶		▼	
Caprine animals	Barely noticeable ▶							
▶					Units (1/6 inch) used in printing			

Raincoat material	▼	Convex shape that narrows toward a point	▼	Relieves	Round bread that opens into a pocket	▼	Extremely	▼
⌐								
Essential		Monk's cubicle		Part of a tennis match	Cease		Powerful herbivore with a horned snout	
⌐		▼		▼	▼		▼	
Adjust again after an initial failure	▶					Root vegetable		Placed in the middle
Chum	Plea of being elsewhere		Subject	▶		▼		▼
⌐	▼		Having negative qualities	Section of glass	▶			
Face-to-face (3-1-3)		Satisfy com-pletely	▼	Item of underwear	Master Weasley, friend of Harry Potter	▶		
⌐		▼		▼			Female repro-ductive cells	
Asked	▶				Not either	▶	▼	
⌐			Play truant from work or school (coll)					
Morsel	Consume	▶			Fill out	▶		

Basic monetary unit of the Philippines	▼	Gleamed	▼	Departs	▼	Marked by sound judgment	▼	Imparted
Intelligible only to the initiated ►	▼							
H Rider Haggard novel ►			Islamic ruler		Flavour			Sacred song
►			▼		▼		▼	
Manner of marching with legs straight (5,4)	Social insect		Grumbles ►					
Commences ►	▼						Restaurant	
Floor on a boat		Discontinue	Honey-badger of Africa and southern Asia ►				▼	
►		▼		Shaft of light ►				
Talked loquacious nonsense	Basic monetary unit of Latvia		Corrosion-resistant malleable metallic element	Owned		Chafe		Expire
►	▼		▼		▼		▼	
World's largest continent ►				Swiss canton, home to William Tell ►				
Incline ►				Informal farewell remark ►				

Decree that prohibits something	▼	Force out	▼	Magnificent	Noisy quarrel	▼	Desist	Liable
Floating aimlessly ►	▼				▼		Prolonged depression of spirits	▼
⚑			Gambol ►				▼	
Joint protected in front by the patella	Low wall along the edge of a roof	▼						
⚑				Harry ___, famous escape artist		Hawaiian floral garland		Pasture
Fired a bullet	Standard monetary unit of Burma		Conforming to Islamic dietary laws	▼		▼		▼
Oil used as fuel in lamps ►	▼							
Asian temple		Mentally or physically infirm with age	Domesticated bovine animals		Gelid ►			
⚑		▼	▼			Above average in size		Informal word used to signify agreement
Travel slowly, as a plane down a runway ►					Lad ►	▼		▼
Native of Muscat, for example	Person who is not a Jew	▼						
⚑					Pain or discomfort ►			

Tibetan priest	▼	Iridescent coating on the inside of a shell	▼	Deliver a blow with the foot	▼	As good as	▼	Ecru
Lively ►		▼						
Water-proof raincoat (abbr) ►				Stride		Hoard		Organic compound
►				▼		▼		▼
Behind the scenes in a theatre	Not allowed to continue to bat or run		Domesti-cates ►					
Dropsy ►	▼						Detection device	
Sicilian volcano		Sound	Temporary police force ►				▼	
►		▼		Person who employs something ►				
Most slender or flimsy	Boy		Animal trap	Mown grass used as fodder		Hour at which something is due (inits)		Male cat
►	▼		▼	▼		▼		▼
Continent ►					Also ►			
Declare untrue ►					Provide with weapons ►			

181

Statement of beliefs	Fabric made of compressed matted fibres	▼	Coin equal to one hundredth of a rouble	▼	Rush	▼	Weight unit / Be obliged to repay	▼
▼					In addition ▶		▼	
Curriculum ___, summary of work history	Brother of George Gershwin		Edible crustacean ▶ / Equine animal					
▼	▼		▼		Grown boys / Greek letter			
Idiots	Beehive of straw ▶ / Marked by secrecy		▶		▼		Overnight condensation	
▼		▼		Spread hay ▶ / Weal on the skin			▼	Watchman
Comedy characterised by improbable situations	Cockeyed		Walks through water ▶ / Stick					▼
▼			▼		Ram's mate ▶ / ___ of the valley			
Fitting exactly (of clothing) (4-5)	High in stature / London borough ▶					Concert	Meat cut from the thigh of a pig	
▼	▼				▼		▼	▼
Adam's wife ▶ / Veneration				Prevaricator ▶				
▼		Diminutive in size ▶						

179

Border	▼	Gas used to fill light bulbs	Undress	▼	Argument opposed to a proposal	Fourth letter of the Greek alphabet	▼	Diameter of a tube or gun barrel
Lower part of an interior wall ▶	▼	▼			Female deer ▶	▼		
Machine processing materials by crushing ▶								Grow old
⚑				Curt or disdainful rejection (5-3)	Field covered with grass			▼
Implores	Celestial path ▶			▼			Green vegetable	
⚑					Chimpan-zee, for example ▶		▼	
Contributor	High male voice	Partially opened flower ▶				Drag behind		Member of a nomadic people
⚑	▼				Children's game ▶	▼		▼
Instances	Perennial herb with bitter-tasting leaves	Of a female ▶					Body of salt water	
Group of three ▶	▼				Snake ▶	▼		
⚑			Travels by plane ▶					
Second person pronoun	Brownie ▶				Not of the clergy ▶			

Biased way of presenting something	▼	Was certain	Official who is expected to ensure fair play	▼	Untidy, dis-organised	▼	Pillar	▼
L					Flurry ►			
Pig, hog		Keen on	Impene-trable mist ►				Plea of being elsewhere	
L		▼			Nineteenth letter of the Greek alphabet ►		▼	
Animal kept as a domestic pet	Scour a surface		Domain ►					
L	▼		Deities		Alcoholic spirit ►			
One stroke over par in golf ►			▼			Mortal		One of the Seven Dwarfs
Under-garment worn by women		Number of players in a baseball team		Nymph who fell in love with Narcissus	Concealed ►	▼		▼
L		▼		▼			Female repro-ductive cells	
Flat round object ►					Cleaning implement ►		▼	
F			Retch ►	►				
Japanese school of Buddhism	Inflated feeling of personal worth				Word indicating a negative answer ►			

181

Chagrin	▼	Cutting instrument	▼	Garden tool for cutting grass on lawns	Opposed to	▼	French word meaning 'father'	▼
⌐								
Capable of producing an intended result		Gratis		Holder	Item used to carry many cups at once		Blood vessels	
⌐		▼		▼			▼	
Departure from what is ethically acceptable	►					Capital of the Isle of Man		Attains
Number, XXI in Roman numerals (6-3)	Interlace		Point directly opposite the zenith	►		▼		▼
⌐	▼							
Bringing to a stop		Molten rock	Row or layer		Large nation (inits)	►		
⌐		▼	▼				Section of a play	
Egotistical	►				Sixth note in the tonic sol-fa scale	►	▼	
►					Top card	►		
Dam	Takes into custody	►						

185

Beige	Chilly	Straight sword with a narrow blade	▼	Lightly strikes a golf ball	Projecting edge of a roof	Stony-broke	▼	Blatant
⌐	▼	▼		Detect ▶	▼	▼		
Scottish bread ▶								Fruiting spike of a cereal plant
Choose ▶				Climbing plant ▶				▼
⌐							Com-pletely	
Shine wetly	Slanted lettering		Recog-nition	Assistant	⌐		▼	
⌐	▼		▼	▼		Celebrity	Milky-white gem		Conse-quence
About		Small wave on the sur-face of a liquid ▶				▼		▼
⌐					Baby's napkin		Means of returning something by post (inits)	
Cooked in an oven		Corrupt morally ▶			▼		▼	
⌐				Country once called Persia ▶				
Group of islands, capital Suva		Medicinal pill ▶						

186

Russian monarch	Gyrate	On fire	▼	Delicate, fragile	Relating to iron	Bottomless gulf or pit	▼	Portico or roofed colonnade
◣	▼	▼		Destiny ►	▼	▼		
Innocuous or inert medication ►								Immoral act
Three, as written in Roman numerals ►				Scandinavian rugs ►			▼	
◤							Before, poetically	
Fishermen	New personification of a familiar idea		Designating sound from two sources	Portent ►			▼	
◤	▼		▼	Chopper		Blockade		Deprives of the use of a limb, cripples
Feline animals		Bunch of cords fastened at one end ►		▼		▼		▼
◤					Symbol used in Morse code		Wander from a direct course	
Milky plant substance that coagulates		Cash in ►			▼		▼	
◤				Man-eating giant ►				
London art gallery		Freshwater carnivorous mammals ►						

184

Decree ___, stage in divorce pro- ceedings	▼	Daily written record / Gaffe	▼	Mark (~) placed over the letter 'n' in Spanish	▼	Yearn / Bureau- cracy (3,4)	▼	Poet / Hot springs
►			▼	Steep rugged rock or cliff	►	▼		▼
Com- pletely sane (coll) (3,5)	►							
Disen- cumber	►		Swirl / Light- sensitive membrane	►				
►				▼	Sir Walter ___ English explorer		Female siblings	
More active than normal (coll)	Thin, scanty	Bad accident involving vehicles (4-2)	Rub out	►	▼		▼	
►	▼	▼	Odd-toed ungulate / Capacious bag					
Snake / Deficient in humane feelings	►		▼					
On your own	►					Falsehood		Bunkum
Merchant who sells goods to the public	►					▼		▼
Girl's name / Edible mushroom	►			Banking system	►			
►			Body part between the neck and the diaphragm	►				

185

Acorn-producing plant (3,4)	▼	Strong wind	Impulse	▼	Direction of the rising sun	▼	That woman's	Important North Atlantic food fish
►					▼		Greek letter	▼
Unhappy		Round vegetable	Greta ___, film star (1905-1990) ►				▼	
►		▼						
One who is playfully mischievous	Large wading bird		Sweet Madeira wine	Provide in a continuous or insistent way		Secure with a wooden pin		Allege
►	▼		▼	▼	Step in dancing (especially in ballet) ►	▼		▼
In a poor way		Succulent plant ►					Express	
►					___ Fawkes, Gunpowder Plot schemer ►		▼	
Spiders' nets		Fatal disease of cattle (inits)		Distort, buckle	▼	Prevarication		Type of poem
►		▼		Lowest female singing voice ►		▼		▼
Dull colour	Arranged in close-packed rows ►							
►				French word meaning 'father' ►				

Cut off with the teeth / Diadem	▼	Poisonous metallic element	Not good / Coarse file	▼	Dressing often served with fish (7,5)	▼		Altitude	▼
◣		▼	▼		Shortened forename of US president Lincoln ▶				
Dealer ▶								Drama set to music	
◤				Occurring within an institution or community ▼	Duvet warmth rating ▶		▼		
Cape	Inscription on a tombstone ▶								
US painter	Capital of Cuba		Blur		Soak (flax or hemp) in water to soften it ▶				
◣	▼		▼						Supernatural being in Muslim folklore ▼
Pinnacle ▶					Mournful ▶				
Composer, Joseph (1732–1809)	Waste product useful as a fertiliser ▶							Menagerie	
◣					Israeli sub-machine-gun ▶		▼		
Belly button	French word for 'boy' ▶								
◣					Longest division of geological time ▶				

187

Buddhist leader who once ruled Tibet (5,4)	▼	Instances	▼	Recipient of money	Follower of Hitler	▼	Disturb the composure of	▼
▼								
Piece of rock or metal from outer space		Friar associated with Robin Hood		Strange	Gather, as of crops		Lake and popular resort area of Nevada, USA	
▼		▼		▼	▼		▼	
Leather with a napped surface	▼				Husband or wife of a reigning monarch			Feature
Hard durable wood	Plant also known as the century plant		Russian country house	▼		▼		▼
▼	▼		Abbreviation for the tenth month	Having little money	▼			
Wealthy and privileged people (coll) (3,4)		Move in large numbers	▼	Yob deterrent (inits)	Web	▼		
▼	▼			▼			Wheat-like cereal plant	
Examines carefully	▼				Imaginary monster or ogre	▼	▼	
▼			Mineral	▼				
Charge	Sound made by a cow	▼			Quoits target	▼		

188

George Bernard ___, playwright	▼	In the current fashion or style (1,2,4)	Mineral / High male voice	▼	Bias (3-9)	▼	Country, capital Stockholm	▼
Cold sea fog ▶		▼	▼		At once ▶			
Verbally report or maintain ▶							Battery terminal	
▶				Came to a conclusion	Melancholy ▶		▼	
Hit swiftly with a violent blow	Accumulation deposited by a glacier ▶			▼				
Acted as a go-between ▶	Firstborn		Breathe in		Put on (clothing) ▶			
▶	▼		▼					Weak cry of a young bird
Transparent optical device ▶					Abbreviation for the 12th month of the year ▶			▼
One who eats no animal or dairy products		Tusk ▶					Large brownish-green parrot of N Zealand	
▶					To stretch out ▶		▼	
Warhorse	Tenant ▶							
▶					Plant juice ▶			

189

Section of writing	▼	Keen	▼	Cooked in an oven	Molten rock	▼	Item of footwear	▼
◣								
Make merry		Delicate, woven and decorative fabric		Morsel	Protective covering of a building		Two times	
◣		▼		▼	▼		▼	
Medium for communication						Pieces of cloth used to mend a hole		Placed in the middle
Expend	Partial darkness		Subject matter of a conversation ▶			▼		▼
◣	▼		Make correspond or harmonise	Point towards ▶				
Promoting peace		Birthday missive	▼	Destiny	Cardinal number ▶			
◣		▼		▼			Long and distinct period of history	
Information ▶					Of a female ▶		▼	
◣			In that place ▶					
For every	Gaming cube ▶				Unhappy ▶			

193

190

Held back

Distinctive and stylish elegance

Regularly go round to maintain security

Lost (2,3)

Seeped

Cunning

Ban or prohibition

Moulding, in the form of the letter S

Spend money like water (coll) (4,3)

Move the head in agreement

Had a meal

Ancient biblical city

One of four playing cards in a deck

Disen-tangle

Small sachet used to make a drink

Acid found in vinegar

Mixer drink

Defunct

Limbs used for flying

Seed-cases with hooks or prickles

Book of maps

Construc-tion built by a spider

Grand-mother

___ de cologne, perfumed liquid

Assigned to a station

Craftsman who prepares skins and hides

Gelling agent

Dress worn primarily by Hindu women

Population count

Move to music	▼	Acquired knowledge	Tatters	▼	This place	Fruits of the palm tree	▼	Covering for a wheel
Prior to a specified time ►	▼	▼			▼			Taxis
Close ►				Continuous portion of a circle	►		▼
Container for a bird ►				Beverage ►			
►			Admiration	Inactive		Centre of a storm	
Belonging to that woman	Because	Gets up ►	▼	▼		▼	
Stitched ►	▼				Brought to a conclusion		Unit of currency
►		Nap ►			▼		▼
Child	Unspecified object	Livestock enclosure ►				Organ of hearing	
Block of soap ►	▼			Hideout ►		▼	
►		Free from dirt or impurities ►					
Chaps	Hitherto ►			Remove moisture ►			

Capital of Kansas / Scented liquid	▼	Finds / Hollow, bag-like structure	▼	Part of a bed	▼	Superior tea grade / Con-taminate	▼	Tirades
▼		▼				▼		▼
Tap lightly ▶ / Illusory feat				Bangla-deshi coin ▶ / Long rod				
▼				▼				
Small pastry dish usually used as a canapé	Ice cream container ▶ / Mystic symbols						Fills with high spirits	
▼		▼					▼	
Judo level	Employs ▶ / Bouquet					Conscious, aware		Bring into play
▼	▼		Corrode, as with acid	Cut-price event ▶ / Singing couple		▼		▼
Marsh plant ▶ / Propose a theory			▼	Candle-making substance ▶ / Prune				
▼				▼				
German composer (1685–1750)	Kitchen appliance ▶		Persis-tently annoying person					
▼			▼					

Baby's bed	▼	Agent that assists colonic irrigation	Glide over snow	▼	Gaffer	Concert place	Layabouts	▼
Explained or answered ►	▼	▼						
Printing fluids ►				Mysterious		Waterfall slide		
►				▼		▼		
Bowing as a sign of reverence	Eldest son of Queen Elizabeth II		State of being poorly illuminated	Major coal mining region in Germany ►				
Insignia used by the medical profession ►	▼		▼					
Person who promotes armed conflict		Destroy completely		Attack		Frame of iron bars to hold a fire		Interprets words
►		▼		▼		▼	▼	▼
Participant in a race ►							University degrees (inits)	
Fibs ►				Sleeveless outer garment worn by Arabs ►		▼		
►				Small amount ►				
Closely crowded together		Emphasis ►						

194

Old form of the word 'you' / Present	▼	Of the greatest possible degree	Type of plane / Got up	▼	Word-and-definition books	▼	Wrote	▼
◣		▼	▼		Decorate with frosting ▶			
Characteristic of another part of the world ▶						Tree which produces berries in autumn		
▶			Excused, let off	Number ▶		▼		
Allows	Cold-blooded vertebrate ▶		▼					
Thin pliable sheet of material	Goes in		Earlier in time		Curious ▶			
◣	▼		▼					Appetising
'Children in ___', annual BBC appeal ▶					Products of human creativity ▶			▼
Acidic fruit		Digit ▶					Plumbing fixture	
◣					Of a thing ▶		▼	
Enquired		Replicate ▶						
◣					Undercover agent ▶			

Shrub with large fragrant tubular flowers	▼	Exposes to view / Be fully aware of	Act presumptuously	▼	Non-flowering plant	Bring out an official document	▼	Cook in an oven
		▼	▼			▼		Bark in a high-pitched tone
Back end ►					Outer space as viewed from Earth ►			▼
Deserve by one's efforts ►					Catch sight of			
►				Nazi secret police	Highest volcano in Europe		Craft of extraterrestrial origins (inits)	
___ of Man or Wight, for example	Large artery		Urge a horse to go faster (3-2) ►	▼	▼		▼	
Boon ►	▼					Perfume		Communion plate
►			Spy ►			▼		▼
Female deer		Append	Small amount ►				Country, capital Washington DC (inits)	
Informal farewell remark (2-2) ►		▼			Available ►		▼	
►			Brief stop ►					
Evil	Singing couple ►				Directed or controlled ►			

196

Head ornament	Platform	▼	Flour and water dough	▼	Water ice on a wooden stick	▼	Cow's milk-gland / Baby's clothes	▼
⌐					Ancient ▶		▼	
Boon	Hollow, flexible, bag-like structure		Cold vegetable dish / Sin ▶					
⌐	▼		▼	Strong washing solution / Chum ▶				
Plant family that includes the maple	Narrow sword ▶ / Printed mistake			▼				
⌐	▼		Appropriate ▶ / Mix of fog and smoke					Annoy continually or chronically
Rebound after hitting	Away	Arboreal mammal ▶ / Stew	▼					▼
⌐	▼	▼		Leguminous plant ▶ / Pleasant				
Beauty parlour ▶ / Disputative				▼	Belonging to us	Swiss canton, home to William Tell		
⌐					▼	▼		
Twosome ▶ / Dreaming state (inits)			Form into a curved or spiral shape					
⌐			Creepy ▶					

200

Gone by	▼	Breaks with established customs	▼	Bear, convey	Protester stationed outside a place of work	▼	Position in a social hierarchy	Swindle
Italian brandy made from residue of grapes	▶	▼			▼		Professional charges	▼
▶				Gen (abbr) ▶		▼		
South African of Dutch descent	Large coarse fern ▶							
▶				Occidental	Hallucinogenic drug (inits)		Border of cloth doubled back and stitched	
Watery part of milk	In one's sleeping place		Celtic language	▼		▼		▼
Things of material value or usefulness	▼ ▶						Fatuous, mindless	
Repeat aloud from memory		Emulate	Man's name, the Russian form of John		Darken ▶	▼		
▶		▼				Sleeping place		Large cask for beer or wine
Bird symbolising peace	▶				Table-tennis racquet	▼		▼
Errol ___, swashbuckling film star	Upstart ▶							
▶					Hideout ▶			

Venomous snake		Apprentice	Drudge		Chimney-pot cover	Carrying weapons		Handle
Stool to rest the feet of a seated person								Lacking hair
Hilltop					Steal			
Barrier of a horizontal bar and supports					Quali-fication (inits)			
				Male donkey	Competent		Important timber or shade tree	
Be unsuc-cessful	Ms Minogue		Fatigued					
Cubes of meat cooked on a skewer						Relative by marriage (2-3)		Chum
			Ascend					
Strong washing solution		Spherical object	Range of knowledge				Form of address to a man	
US state, capital Des Moines					Hallucino-genic drug (inits)			
			Characteri-sed by dignity and propriety					
That girl	Form of transport, double-decker				Humorous			

Cap's peak / Floor covering (abbr)	▼	Close	▼	Main artery	▼	Bard / Biblical son of Abraham	▼	Azure / Ghostly apparition
▶		▼		Greases ▶		▼		▼
Dishes out (food) (5,2) ▶								
Cereal grass ▶			Old-fashioned 'you' / Method ▶					
▶				▼	Distinguished		Italian port	
Tapestry used as a wall hanging	Point in orbit	Protection	Leavening agent ▶		▼		▼	
▶	▼	▼	Slander / Roofed colonnade ▶					
Nitrogen, for example / Lozenge ▶		▼						
In many cases or instances ▶						Pitch		High-pitched bark
Mathematics of points, lines and curves ▶						▼		▼
7th Greek letter / Slightly insane ▶			Name of the dog in 'Peter Pan' ▶					
▶			Implement used to sharpen razors ▶					

203

200

Basic unit of currency in Nicaragua	▼	Run easily	Carries out	▼	Makes a wager	▼	Sum charged for riding in a bus	Animal doctor (abbr)
					▼		Egyptian goddess of fertility	▼
Enquiry into the finances of a person (5,4)		General name for beer	Creepy ▶				▼	
	▼							
Sanctify	Andean mammal		Male child of your spouse and an ex-partner	Drunkard		One of the supports for a table		Barrier that contains the flow of water
	▼			▼	Hallucinogenic drug (inits) ▶	▼		▼
Military trainee		Heavy book ▶					Divisions of quantity	
					Sticky tree sap ▶		▼	
Idiots		To and ___		Homework	▼	Basque terrorists (inits)		Web
		▼		Keep in check ▶		▼		▼
By an unknown author, in short	Ornament made of ribbon, given as an award	▶						
				Former ▶				

204

Smallest quantity / Asian peninsula	▼	Admonish	Carbon dioxide, for example / Alleviate	▼	Aggressive or warlike behaviour	▼	Joyful	▼
⌐		▼			Measure of cloth ▶			
Plant with spiny bracts ▶							Avoid	
⌐			Sliced assorted chilled meats (4,4) ▼	Allow ▶			▼	
Restricts the number or amount of	Come into posses-sion of ▶							
Partied	Raise in a relief		Go by		Wander aimlessly in search of pleasure ▶			
⌐	▼		▼					Blossom ▼
Merge, blend together ▶					Jewish title, the equivalent of 'Mr' or 'Sir' ▶			▼
Beaver-like animal		Dull pain ▶					Former French gold or silver coin	
⌐					Prefix meaning recent or modern ▶		▼	
Cinders	Ornamen-tal plaster used to cover walls ▶							
⌐				Exclama-tion of pleasure in anticipa-tion of food ▶				

202

Groom's partner	Unit of length equal to 1760 yards	▼	Fourth letter of the Greek alphabet	▼	Spinal bone	▼	Fatuous / The day before	▼
◣					To the full extent (poetically) ▶		▼	
Large box with a lid	Possessed		Insect grub / Timid ▶					
◣	▼				Number / Principle of the universe ▶			
Swirl		Dislike intensely / Fortune ▶			▼		Burned remains	
◣		▼	Arab garment / Rum and water mix ▶				▼	Celebration of the Resurrection of Christ
Mean person	Land surrounded by water		Furze / Long periods of time ▶	▼				▼
◣	▼		▼	Norwegian pop group / Exclamation ▶				
Crouch, bow / Catapult ▶				▼	Score	Poem with complex stanza forms		
◣						▼	▼	
Printing measures / Pigs' home ▶			Align oneself with ▶					
◣			Express ▶					

206

Tight-fitting hats	Expression used at the end of a prayer	Central American canal	▼	Digression	Clear	Fountain nymph	▼	Implores
▼	▼	▼		Singles ►		▼		
Letter carrier's pouch ►								Beard found on a bract of grass ▼
Conclude ►				Travel permit ►				
▼						___ and buts, objections ▼		
Deficiency of red blood cells	Motive		Circlet of leaves	Chief Norse god ►				
▼	▼		▼	Clairvoyance (inits) ▼		Notions ▼		Limited periods of time ▼
Sketch	Express opposition ►							
▼					21st letter of the Greek alphabet ▼		Products of human creativity ▼	
Earnings	Seem ►							
▼				Injury ►				
Protrude the lips		Heaves upwards ►						

207

204

Incinerate	Extra-terrestrial craft (inits)	Proportion	▼	Erstwhile	Having two parts	Hydro-phobia	▼	Mythological beauty, __ of Troy
▶	▼	▼		Depicted ▶	▼	▼		
Relating to reality ▶								Chop
▶				In one's sleeping place ▶				▼
Doves' home	Fair-haired		Russian pancake ▶					
▶	▼		▼	Units (1/6 inch) used in printing	Application		Strained, filtered	
Double-reed woodwind instrument		Creamy dish ▶			▼		▼	
▶				Pincer		Let have for a limited time		George __, footballer who died in 2005
Male children		That man	Famous person (abbr) ▶	▼		▼		
Indian dish made of split pulses ▶	▼				Biblical first woman ▶			
▶			Woman's name, old-fashioned ▶					
Floral garland	Common gull ▶				Banned insecticide (inits) ▶			

205

Oven for firing pottery	Gall	Immature insect	↓	Ancient Peruvian	State of deep unconsciousness	Croaky	↓	Scottish mountain of at least 3,000 feet
→	↓	↓		Thick-bodied European river fish →	↓	↓		
Nocturnal mammal native to North America →								Nautical speed unit
→				Blemish →				↓
Gumbo	Herbivorous lizard of tropical America		British peer of the lowest rank →					
→	↓		↓	Frequently (poetically)	Gentle blow		Underweight	
Informal greeting used on meeting or parting		Dense woodland →		↓	↓		↓	
→				Dissenting clique		Put down		Remove
Cousin's mother	Have	Cleave →	↓	↓		↓		↓
Bulge or swelling →	↓			Mother of the ancient Irish gods →				
→		Narrow opening admitting light →						
Part of the skull of a vertebrate	Negative word →			Colourant →				

Cherished	Quite	Resound	▼	Movable barrier in a fence or wall	▼	Have to	▼	Gem
L	▼	▼						
Perform ►				In the past		Long raised strip		Skid
Buildings where performances can be presented ►				▼		▼		▼
►			Dress		Not in good health ►			
Which person?		Wintry	▼				Citrus fruit	
►				Dress-making aid	Deity ►		▼	
Con-sequently	Measure of land	Globe ►		▼				
►	▼				River which flows through Hereford	Charged particle		Informal term for a father
Caribbean country		Disen-tangle ►			▼	▼		▼
►				Hindu theistic philosophy and exercise ►				
Streetcar		Made level or straight ►						

207

Outward flow of the tide		Canine film star		Compass point	Hard deposit on the teeth		Length of string	Electrical resistance unit
Very drunk (slang)							Bedtime beverage	
				Curved gateway				
Type of strap on the upper of a shoe (1-3)	Fame							
				Paid positions of regular employ-ment		Bastion		Without any attempt at con-cealment
Girdle	Mixture of ground animal feeds		Biblical brother of Esau					
Commem-oration								
Helper		Sprinkled with seed	'The ___ of March', 2011 film		Small insecti-vorous birds		'Fiddling' Roman emperor	
Brick carrier			Approxi-mation of quantity, degree or worth					
Weapons for firing bullets	Cowboy film							
			Receptacle for a coin					

US mid-western state	Gemstone	Large northern marine mammal	⬛	Recipient of money	Dwelling	Dramas	⬛	Linear units
⬛	▼	▼		Highest point	▼	▼		
Outstan-ding and due to be settled (of money)	▶							Fodder
Alcoholic beverage	▶			Commit-ment to tell the truth ▶				▼
⬛							Food in a pastry shell	
Prior to a specified time	Icon repre-senting a person		Permanent mass of snow on the land	Dress worn primarily by Hindu women	⬛		▼	
⬛	▼		▼	▼	Catch sight of	Bedlam		Having much foliage
Desert garden		Annul ▶				▼		▼
⬛					22nd letter of the Greek alphabet		___ and don'ts, rules of behaviour	
Heavy pole tossed as a test of strength		Stout-bodied insect with a loud sound ▶			▼		▼	
⬛				Animal's foot ▶				
Collection of facts		Exag-geratedly proper ▶						

Merry-go-round	▼	Taverns	▼	Makes a wager	▼	Of the highest quality / Country	▼	Mis-chievous little fairy
►	▼					▼		Anoint with oil
Intestinal parasite / Deep groove	►			Insect stage / Constant	►			▼
Be constantly talking or worrying about	►			▼			Exhibiting vigorous good health	
►			Most noticeable or important		H Rider Haggard novel	►	▼	
Form of transport, double-decker		Succes-sive	►	▼				
►					Alcoholic brew	►		
Virile sort of chap (2-3)		Gaffe		Abbrevia-tion seen after a company's name	▼	Long-eared creature, similar to a rabbit		Absorbed, engrossed
Trunk of a tree	One half of one third / Lyric poem	▼				▼	Can	▼
►	▼			Collection of facts	►		▼	
Have supper / Held back	►				Rend	►		
►				Closely confined	►			

Skilful in movements of the hands	▼	Stomach	▼	Tolerated	Naming word	▼	Offshore territory	▼
▼								
Leeway		Misplace		Common cyst of the skin	Boy's name		Coarse	
▼		▼		▼	▼		▼	
Mountain call ▶						Clawed frog native to Sub-Saharan Africa		Tran-quillised
Lyric poem	Cover with cloth		Con-nected series or group ▶			▼		▼
▼	▼		Important timber or shade tree	Give up ▶				
Hunt cry telling that a fox has been seen (5-2)		Organ located in the chest	▼	Sweet potatoes	Diminutive form of the name Edward ▶			
▼		▼		▼			Ms Braun, Hitler's mistress	
American feline ▶					Domesti-cated animal kept for company ▶		▼	
▶			Light violet colour ▶					
Adult female bird	Oxygen, for example ▶				Mournful			

214

Bullets, etc (abbr)	Person of exceptional learning or wisdom	Musical half notes	▼	Egyptian falcon-headed god	Scandinavian raiders	Held in reserve for future consideration (2,3)	▼	Prescribed selection of foods
◣	▼	▼		Empty area or space	◣	▼		
Flight company ◣								Head of corn
Wildebeest ◣			Toy flown in the wind ◣					▼
◣							Do something	
Caused by an earthquake	Hardened to		Closed political meeting	Approach ◣			▼	
◣	▼		▼	Bathing resort		Bring into play		Morally degraded, sleazy
Flat round object	Things of material value or usefulness ◣			▼		▼		▼
◣					Former Chinese communist leader		Deep groove	
Carve (3,2)	Equipment for taking pictures ◣				▼		▼	
◣			Plant such as the cuckoo pint ◣					
Dandy	Prone to acne ◣							

215

Recess in a church	Flow in a spurt	Leap	▼	Time of life between the ages of 13-19	Cold vegetable dish	Keyboard instrument	▼	Small narrow pointed missile
◣	▼	▼		Unwanted email	◥	▼		
Outdoor (4-3) ▶								Meat cut from the thigh of a pig ▼
Pot ▶				Narrow thin strip of wood ▶				
◤							Grease	
West Germanic language	Hooded waterproof jacket		Aid, be of help	Part of a flower	◥		▼	
◤	▼		▼	▼	Condemn to a grim fate	Apart- ments		Exercises evaluating skill or know- ledge ▼
Epic tales		Muffle, suppress ▶				▼		
◤					Pastry dish		Hawaiian floral garland	
Clump of trees		African antelope ▶			▼		▼	
◤				Individual unit ▶				
Metal food containers		Disser- tation ▶						

216

Arouse interest	▼	Motorcycle rider	▼	Animal with two feet	Female pantomime character	▼	Departed, went	▼
◣								
Preventative measure		Subdue		Subject to laughter or ridicule	Horse colouring		Racket	
◣		▼		▼	▼		▼	
Medium for communication	◣				Start out on a sea voyage (3,4)			Elegant, imposing
Had a meal	Eighth letter of the Greek alphabet		Footing	▶		▼		▼
◣	▼	Alliterative term for a young woman	Bird's construction	▶				
Residue		Small particle of dust		Graven image	Beverage	▶		
◣			▼		▼		Field suitable for grazing by livestock	
Narrated	▶				Beer	▶	▼	
◣			Projecting bay window	▶				
Charge levied on goods or services (inits)	Slippery fish	▶			Put in a horizontal position	▶		

Group of people attractively arranged	▼	Cook in an oven	Line formed by joining two pieces	▼	Prince Consort to Queen Victoria	▼	Plant fibre used in making rope or sacks	Skill
⌞					▼		Acute but unspecific feeling of anxiety	▼
In a position of comfort or rest		Sound made by a dove	Com-munion table	►			▼	
⌞		▼						
Late news inserted into a newspaper (4,5)	Period when a light meal is taken		Gift	Assume a stance, as for artistic purposes		Fleshy pendulous part of the hearing organ		Trans-mitters
⌞	▼		▼	▼		▼		▼
Enclosures for pets		Revolve	►					
⌞					Charitable gifts		Duelling sword	
Cube		Covered with a waterproof coating	►		▼			
⌞				Slow pace of running	►			
One-hundredth of a dollar		Amount	►					
⌞				Looks	►			

215

Release (3,4)	▼	Basic rhythmic unit in a piece of music	Scottish hillside	▼	Swirl	▼	Yield	Marry
⌐				▼			Young girl	▼
Com-pletely lifeless (5-4)		Globe	Become rotten, as of an egg, for example	▶			▼	
⌐		▼						
Cat with a grey or tawny coat mottled with black	Become less intense		Bed covering	Affirmative word		Fuss		Tap lightly
⌐	▼		▼	▼	Veno-mous snake ▶	▼		▼
Small, savoury Spanish snacks		Direct ▶					Ringworm	
⌐				Excessive, extreme (inits) ▶			▼	
Apex		Each and every		Major divisions of time	▼	And so forth (abbr)		Lair
⌐		▼		Tear ▶		▼		▼
Band to tie around the body	Bene-ficiary of a will ▶							
⌐			Examine hastily ▶					

219

216

Indian nursemaid	▼	Hawaiian greeting	Diminutive of Henry	▼	Long-eared creature, similar to a rabbit	Conscious of	Elongated cluster of flowers	▼
Prince or king in India ►		▼	▼			▼		
Resembling wings ►					Scientific instrument that gives a flashing light		Cloth woven from flax	
►					▼		▼	
On a large scale, without discrimination	Buildings for housing vehicles		Quack remedy for ills or diseases	Crop ►				
Death of part of the body ►	▼		▼					
Small bracelet or strap	Know-ledgable about (2,2)		Particular items		Accu-mulate		Be afraid of	
►	▼		▼		▼		▼	
Song of devotion or loyalty ►						Unit of gravita-tional force		
Coagu-lated blood from a wound ►				Grow older ►	▼			
►				Large body of water ►				
Group containing one or more species	Created disorder ►							

Call that signals the military to return to quarters		Gave permission to		Sheep's coat	Gains victory over		Elevated open grassland in southern Africa	
Completely sane (coll) (3,5)								
Golfing device / Endeavoured				Quagmire	End of year school dance in the USA		Long fishes	
Spanish dance in triple time		Girdle / Country, capital Monrovia						
						Ill-treated		Perspires
French priests	Groom's partner		Accumulate / Peers of the realm					
					Epic tale		Intellect	
Take on again / Ethiopian 'dollar'								
				Continent				
Industrious / Large bodies of water								
				Sums up				

Statement of verified information ▼	▼	Pedes-trianised public square	Afghan monetary unit	▼	Escape quickly	Point in the time of a cycle	Be in awe of	▼
Dessert associated with the USA (5,3) ►		▼	▼			▼		
Hint ►					Change		Projection at the end of a piece of wood	
⌐					▼		▼	
Deadlock	Snapped		Make amends for, remedy	Exploiter ►				
Plant pigment converted to vitamin A ►	▼		▼					
Sedi-mentary rock		Name of the dog in 'Peter Pan'		Exorbitant		Arrange		Level betting
⌐		▼		▼		▼		▼
Jimmy ___, 39th President of the USA ►							Charged particle	
Joint protected in front by the patella ►					Expire ►		▼	
⌐					Epoch ►			
Discon-tinue		Rejects with contempt ►						

Indian nursemaid	Abominable snowman	Without usual standards or principles	▼	Tertiary	Painfully desirous of another's assets	Boredom	▼	Measure (out)
►	▼	▼		Scoff ►	▼	▼		
Distinguished	►							Existed, lived
Prominent rock or pile of rocks on a hill	►			Afresh ►				▼
►							Garland	
Avian virus such as H5N1 (4,3)	Transfer a file to a computer at another location		Appliance that corrects dental problems	Greases			▼	
►	▼		▼	Large nation (inits)		Strong sweeping cut		Deflect, fend off
Incandescent lamp		Country, capital Moscow	►	▼		▼		▼
►					Female member of a religious order		Leguminous plant	
Assumed name	Thin slice of toast with savoury food	►		▼		▼		
►				Exploiter ►				
Sum charged for riding in a bus	Shade-giving bonnet	►						

Large African antelope		Preposterous		Cooks slowly and for a long time in liquid		Painful sore	Perfect	
Across the whole country								
				Essential oil obtained from flowers		French river	Possess	
Three-dimensional shape	Engulf							
					Bird that hoots			
Outer layer on bread	Slowly, in musical tempo		Light-weight cord					
			Attack on all sides		One who is playfully mischievous		Propel with a quick movement of the fingers	
Craze	Short underpants							
				Listening organ		Pocket		Pigpen
Undulate	Invasion by pathogenic bacteria							
					Law passed by Parliament			
Ringworm	Awkward							

221

Ascend	Chancy	Highly seasoned fatty sausage	▼	Coloured transparent gemstone	▼	Emergency / Virile chap (2-3)	▼	Nought
◣	▼	▼		Flightless bird ▶		▼		
Person who shoes horses ▶								Breach
Aviate ▶				Mixture of fog and smoke ▶				▼
⚑							Grow older	
Muscular pain	Attained maximum intensity		Breed of monkey	Compass point	⚑		▼	
⚑	▼		▼	▼	Card game	Column, of light for example		Helicopter propeller
Steeple	Large heavy rope for nautical use ▶					▼		▼
⚑					Informer		Strong anger	
Enclosures for pets	Sea channel joining two larger bodies of water ▶			▼			▼	
⚑			Rounded thickly curled hairdo ▶					
List of dishes available	Compositor ▶							

Anger	▼	Citrus fruit	▼	Quantity of paper, 24 or 25 sheets	▼	Brie or Edam, for example	▼	Gelling agent
Coarse food high in fibre but low in nutrients ▶	▼							
▶				Chest bone		Away		Ejects with force
Persian fairy	State of being behind in payments ▶			▼		▼		▼
Laminated metamorphic rock similar to granite ▶							Relevant	
Australian term for a young kangaroo	Prophet		Ecru ▶				▼	
▶	▼		▼	Bear fruit	Condensed water vapour ▶			
Held back, as of breath		Semi-aquatic creature		Belonging to that woman ▶				
▶		▼		Cash machine outside banks (inits)	Underwater vessel (abbr)			Level
High mountain pass ▶				In the quickest time (inits) ▶	▼	▼		▼
Boy ▶ / Directed				Large, edible marine fish ▶				
▶			Deep yellow colour ▶					

Manufacturer of toy bricks	___ de Cologne, perfumed liquid	Huge person	▼	Blood-stained	Indian dish made of split pulses	Gave a clue	▼	Person who drinks alcohol to excess
◣		▼		Arab sailing vessel	▼	▼		
Elongated dirigible powered balloon								Blow gently
◣				Afresh				▼
Wharf	Narcotic drug		Extreme ▶					
◣	▼		▼	Cereal grass	Coat a cake with sugar		Defeat some challenge or person (3,3)	
Travel (2,2)		Among ▶			▼		▼	
◣				Dollar	Native of the country formerly known as Siam			Sediment in wine
Catalogue	Smallest whole number	Asian pepper plant	▼		▼		▼	
Bean curd ▶	▼			Weeding tool ▶				
◣		Make sore by rubbing ▶						
One-hundredth of a yen	Large deer ▶			___ and ___ buts, objections ▶				

		For the purpose of raising money for (2,3,2)	Not any		Pain sometimes experienced by divers	Person moved from a dangerous place		Native of Bangkok, for example
Grate (teeth)								
Ancient Assyrian city on the Tigris								Item used to carry many cups at once
At another time					Charge levied on goods or services (inits)			
Fine grit					Atmosphere			
					Hollow metal device which rings		A person in general	
Starts suddenly, as from fright	Long-distance bus		Delicate, woven and decorative fabric	Floating marker on the water				
Mc-Cullough, writer								Feel
			Sediment in wine					
Couch		Propel in a high arc		Craze		Assistance	Route	
Musical mark indicating the pitch of notes					Beard found on a bract of grass			
			Assumed name					
17th letter of the Greek alphabet	Command				Colourant			

228

225

Engage in a contest		Moved away	Body of water		Pare / Not this!		Swimming pool	
							In the quickest time (inits)	
Contradict		Word indicating a negative answer	Having the leading position					
				In addition				
Bottomless gulf	Sharp part of a knife		Article of clothing for cooler climates	Dis-tressing		Cardinal number		19th letter of the Greek alphabet
					Choose or show a preference			
Assigned to a station		Admonish				Confused scuffle		
					Bird similar to an ostrich			
Vegetable matter used as a fuel		Donkey		Ms Amos, songstress		Inten-tionally so written (used after a word)		Not divisible by two
				Capital of Norway				
Former communist country (inits)	Arranged in close-packed rows							
				Decorated with frosting				

226

Magic spell or charm	▼	Inclined surfaces	▼	Cultivated land as a unit	▼	Carried	▼	Urticaria
Musical work based on a religious text ▶	▼							
Container used to store jam, dried fruit, etc ▶			At the peak of		Lose water or moisture (3,2)			Adjust again after an initial failure
▶			▼		▼		▼	
Officer in charge of a military unit	Former name of Tokyo, Japan		Abrupt ▶					
▶	▼				Pale grey		Mariner	
Sauce typically served with Italian food		Hindu princess	Brief stop ▶		▼		▼	
▶	▼			Ejected saliva from the mouth ▶				
Knowledge gained through tradition	In the month preceding the present one (abbr)		___ and outs, details of a situation	US government unit (inits)		Loud utterance of emotion		Units (1/6 inch) used in printing
Acrobat's one-wheeled bike ▶	▼		▼	▼		▼		▼
▶				Computer storage device (inits) ▶				
Russian pancake		Forest gods ▶						

230

227

Sport with few restrictions on moves	Beads used in prayer	Young newts	▼	Kitchen appliance	▼	Of or relating to the ear	▼	Arm covering
◣	▼	▼						
Away	►			Ailing		Small anchor		Police informers (slang)
Put out of action (by illness)	►			▼		▼		▼
◣					Ms Herzigova, super-model	►		
Aromatic herb		Engineless plane	►					
◣				Epoch, age	Heavy open wagons		Ordered series	
Cattle shed	Chief port of Yemen	Area set back or indented	►	▼			▼	
◣	▼					'It is', poetically		Soak (flax or hemp) in water to soften it
African desert		Encrusta-tion that forms on the teeth and gums	►			▼		▼
◣				Slab found on a roof	►			
Manu-facturer of popular toy bricks		Brown with a reddish tinge	►					

228

Confuse (3,2)	▼	Aggressive and pointed remark	Disciple	▼	Equipment for taking pictures	▼	Thorough-fare	▼
◣					Towards the stern of a ship ►			
Depends on		Boundary, rim	Electrical resistance unit ►				Right-hand page	
◣			▼		Before, poetically ►		▼	
Harass with persistent ridicule	Unit of electric current		Number in a trio ►					
◣	▼		Former unit of money in Italy		Law passed by Parliament ►			
Confused scuffle ►			▼			Ache, long		Believer in God
Patio		Payment by a tenant to a landlord		Land force	Tenth and smallest letter of the Hebrew alphabet ►	▼		▼
◣		▼		▼			Garland of flowers	
Stand up on the hind legs ►					Muham-mad ___, former boxing champion ►		▼	
◣			Adult female horses ►					
Gaelic word meaning a mountain peak	Non-functional replica of something else ►				Egg of a louse ►			

Origin / Gathered, came together	▼	Give a shine to	▼	Compass point	▼	Behave	▼	Extent
▼				▼				
X mark		Cereal grass	►			Simple		Poke or thrust abruptly
▼				Married woman's title (abbr) / Talk wildly	▼		▼	
Field covered with grass		Avenue / Land extent of a farm	►	▼				
▼		▼	Bedding material	Domain / All right	►			
Refuse to work, as a protest	Pungent spice	►	▼	▼			Product of seabirds, used as a fertiliser	
▼						Russian emperor	▼	Chew
Having substance and prompting thought	Hour due (inits) / Consume	►			Pull sharply	▼		▼
▼	▼				Francisco, US city	►		
Grow older / Exacting	►			Name of the dog in 'Peter Pan'	►			
▼				Angry dispute	►			

Old-fashioned form of the word 'you'	▼	Not at the scheduled time	Writing tool / Simple, bare	▼	Force released by nuclear reaction (6,6)	▼	Half asleep	▼
Abode ►			▼		Seaman ►			
All the same, however (4,2) ►							Positively charged electrode	
►				Criminal who commits homicide	Informal term for the mouth ►		▼	
Antlered animal	Residue ►		▼					
Moved briskly or in a panicky way	Crumple		Admini-stration		Affecting shyness ►			
└	▼		▼					Multi-plication
Waterside plant ►					Snare, trap ►			▼
Muslim or Hindu mendicant monk	Unit of heredity found on a chromo-some ►						Source of metal	
└				Computer storage device (inits) ►			▼	
More recent	Deficient in amount or quality ►							
└				Affirmative answer ►				

231

Motivated by ill-will	For a short time	Fibber	▼	Urban centre	▼	Assistant	▼ Hand tool for boring holes
L	▼	▼					
Mental capacity	►			Dandy		Go to see some person or place for a short time	Less common
Allergic reaction to pollen (3,5)	►		▼		▼		▼
►		Practitioner of rigorous self-discipline		Lyricist, —— Gershwin	►		
Melody		Imitates ►	▼			Breakfast food	
►			Large nation (inits)	Water in a solid state ►		▼	
Professional charges	Slide	Fast coastal patrol boat ►	▼				
►	▼				Partially opened flower	Abbreviation seen after the name of a company	Definite article
Cinders		Medicinal pill ►			▼	▼	▼
►			Mormon state of the USA ►				
Equipment for reproducing sound (2-2)		Embrace lovingly ►					

This is a blank crossword grid puzzle.

Containing salt	▼	University degrees (inits)	▼	Card game similar to écarté	Footing	▼	Cuts into cubes	▼
Capital of the United Arab Emirates (3,5) ►	▼							
Resin-like substance ► / Food turner (4,5)				Contract, become smaller	Incline		Three-dimensional shape	
►				▼	▼		▼	
Groups containing one or more species	Breed of monkey ► / Love-in-a-mist plant							
►						Twisted at an angle		Paper handkerchief
Cause to act, encourage (3,2)	Transplant		Gusset ► / Huge sea			▼		▼
►	▼		▼		Part of the ear		Stony waste matter	
Foolhardy ► / Bundle of hay or straw					▼		▼	
►				Nocturnal birds of prey ►				
Fiery torch ► / Diminutive boy's name								
►				Border ►				

233

Pit viper / Bitter alkaloid in coffee	▼	Feeble-ness	Help develop and grow	▼	Third son of Adam and Eve	Nigerian monetary unit	▼	Diesel oil used in cars and lorries (acronym)
⌐		▼				▼		Fluid-filled sac
Canter ▶					Bow ▶			▼
⌐					Clinging plant ▶			
Save up for future use / Ignited ▶				Hobby	Religious song		And not	
Indian or African animal ▶				▼			▼	
Digress ▶						Book of maps		Believe in
⌐			Astute ▶			▼		▼
None in particular		Of a thing	Explosive initials! ▶				Yoko ___, artist	
Bird of New Zealand ▶		▼			Ferrigno, 'Incredible Hulk' actor ▶		▼	
⌐			Has in mind ▶					
Risk money on the outcome of an event	Girl's name ▶				Chronic drinker ▶			

234

Take for granted / Moving staircase	▼	African lily / Engine part	▼	Marine food fish of the North Atlantic	▼	Blanket / Article of faith	▼	Long raised strip
⌐	▼					▼		▼
volatile / Stole	►			Strauss, jeans manufacturer	►			
⌐								
Qualification (inits) / Currency unit	►			Mass of ice / Frequently (poetically)	►			
⌐			Known / Awake	► ▼			Able to absorb fluids	►
Extract (metals) by heating	Vessel of planks / Disease of animals	►	▼			Mother-of-pearl	▼	Earnings
⌐	▼				At once / Airborne soldier (abbr)	► ▼		▼
Devoured / Access	►			10th letter of the Hebrew alphabet	⌐			
⌐				▼	Part of a gear wheel	►		
Travel (2,2) / Of a female	►				Regret	►		
⌐			Clothing	►				

235

Venomous hooded snake

Act of returning to Earth's atmosphere (2-5)

Apex

Rope

Paving stones

Honk

Recount

Sea creature / Ale

Rented out

Study

Primate

Fund of money put by as a reserve (4,3)

A long way off

Append

Slope

Cubicle

Belonging to the organ of smell

Short

Man-made fibre

Harnessed together

Pale yellowish to yellowish brown

__ Orbison, singer of 'Crying'

Sweet potato

Attempt

'All about __', film starring Bette Davis

Printed characters

Basic unit of money in Albania

Item worn on the hand

Expression of surprise or sudden comprehension

Drinking vessel

Diminutive of Edward

236

Fund-raising event	Colour of un-bleached linen	Zodiacal sign	▼	Cap with no brim or peak	Postures assumed by models	French river	▼	Grooved tooth of a venomous snake
⌐	▼	▼		Scheme ►	▼	▼		
Animated film ►								Zero
Strong-scented perennial herb ►				Gesture ►				▼
⌐							Side sheltered from the wind	
Additional	Untwist		Rubs out, obliterates	Long detailed story	►		▼	
⌐	▼		▼	▼	Deal, trade	Hits with an open hand		Cathedral dignitaries
Mulls over, ponders	Brought up ►					▼		▼
⌐					Germanic invader		Fish eggs	
Lean end of the neck	North African desert ►				▼		▼	
⌐				Atop ►				
Lively style of jazz music, swing	Detects auto-matically ►							

240

Daze	▼	Greek muse of love poetry	▼	Prevents (from doing something)	▼	Skeletal	▼	Felt concern or interest
Reckless and impetuous person ▶	▼							
Receptacle for ashes after a cremation ▶			Plant fibre used to make rope		Formal title used to a woman ▼		Devil ▼	
⌐								
Without remorse	Toilet (coll)		Circumvent	▶				
Overhung threateningly ▶	▼						Want strongly	
Daring		Creased	Spanish national art gallery in Madrid	▶			▼	
⌐		▼	Sign of something about to happen ▶					
Excellent	Mature		Trail, track	(They) exist		Vat		Branch of the UK police force (inits)
⌐	▼		▼	▼		▼		▼
Cogwheel ▶					Mr Geller, spoonbender ▶			
Boundary ▶					Sleeping place ▶			

241

238

Biblical twin of Jacob	▼	Arouse or excite feelings and passions	Common type of tree — Course of existence	▼	Female siblings of one's spouse (7-2-3)	▼	Insist	▼
Part of a window-frame ▶		▼	▼		Nickname of US president Eisen-hower ▶			
Feeling of ill-will arousing active hostility ▶							Hand joint	
▶				Exercises authori-tative power over	Former US airline (1930–2001) (inits) ▶	▼		
High tight collar	Reading desk ▶			▼				
Tedious monotony	Fleet of warships		Affiance		Disen-cumber ▶			
▶	▼		▼					Detect a circum-stance or entity auto-matically
Charter ▶					Of a thing ▶			▼
Former Portu-guese province in China		Broad smile ▶					Consumed	
▶					System that links computers (inits) ▶	▼		
Gateaux	Shows malicious satisfaction ▶							
▶					Tiny ▶			

242

239

Magic spell / Scottish river	▼	Adult male chicken	Which person? / Uncouth person	▼	Capable of being cleansed in water	▼	Popular pet rodents	▼
◣		▼	▼		Farm-house cooker	▶		
Full of exultant happiness	▶						Whatso-ever	
◣				Use water to remove soap	Features	▶	▼	
Large black bird	Retainer	▶		▼				
Warm dry wind that blows in the Alps	Of a sphere, flattened at the sides		Removes the calyx of a strawberry		Cheerio			
◣	▼		▼		Dripping wet		Commit to memory	
Capital of Belgium	▶				▼		▼	
Ancient Semitic deity		Sicken				Cane spirit		Public transport vehicle
◣	▼		Seize suddenly	▶		▼		▼
"It is", poetically / Slippery fish	▶		Religious teacher	▶				
◣		Songs of praise	▶					

243

Furious, savage	Make attractive or lovable	Harness strap	▼	US state, capital Des Moines	▼	Bake in a kiln so as to harden	▼	Roman province at the time of Christ
⌐	▼	▼						
Novel ►			Fluffy scarf of feathers		Assig-nation		Step	
Disorder of the meta-bolism ►			▼		▼		▼	
►		Eyeglass		Common rodent ►				
One-hundredth of a yen	Numerous ►	▼				Bone of the forearm		
►			Long and distinct period of history	___ Lanka, country ►		▼		
Conse-quently	Muslim prayer leader	Flower 'juice' ►	▼					
►	▼			Definite article	French word for 'no'		Not anti!	
Junior	Perennial herb also known as nepeta ►			▼	▼		▼	
►			Three thousand six hundred seconds ►					
Release after a security has been paid	All the same, however (4,2) ►							

Flour and water dough	▼	Disgrace	Armoured combat vehicle	▼	Globes	Falls	▼	Bitter quarrel between two parties
With legs stretched far apart ▶	▼		▼			▼		Group noun for quails or larks
Blackleg ▶					Chafe ▶			
Prepares leather ▶					Lyric poem ▶			
▶				Novelty	Continent		Golf peg	
Financial institution	Coat in fat		Awful ▶	▼	▼		▼	
Traditional pantomime tale, "___ in the Wood" ▶	▼					Con-tending		Large group of fish
▶			Married women ▶			▼		▼
Buddy		None in particular	Word indicating a negative answer ▶				Chemical which carries genetic info (inits)	
Carry ▶		▼			Artificial language, a simplification of Esperanto ▶		▼	
▶			Plant with pods used as a laxative ▶					
Japanese school of Buddhism	Affirmative answer ▶				Young woman (coll) ▶			

242

Practical	Bring to humbler state	Waterless	▼	City in northern India	▼	Become less clearly visible	▼	Exists
⌐	▼	▼						
Make a mistake ►				Con-stricting snake		Narrow to a point		Garment worn on the upper half of the body
Disorder marked by an inability to produce insulin ►				▼		▼		▼
⌐			Old soldier		Deciduous tree ►			
Partially opened flower	Piece of leather forming a shoe's front upper		▼				Italian town, birthplace of Saint Francis	
⌐				Com-plexion	Sense organ ►		▼	
DNA unit	Hollywood actress, Cameron ___	Physio-logical need to drink	►	▼				
⌐	▼				Male sheep, ram	Boat built by Noah		Granny
French goodbye		Hang on to ►			▼	▼		▼
⌐				Latin name of two con-stellations ►				
Showy and festive party		Serviette made of cloth ►						

246

Arrowword puzzle grid:

- Hour at which something is due (inits)
- Fisherman
- Bathroom fixture
- Complied
- Coloured part of the eye
- Type of lettuce
- Maker and alterer of garments
- Rivulet
- Brand name of a ballpoint pen
- Group of musicians
- Bible book that tells of Adam and Eve
- Food provider
- Directed
- Curious
- Mud deposited in an estuary
- Afflicts
- Instrument played with a bow
- Series of arches supported by columns
- Flip to a vertical position
- Division of Ireland
- Adult male deer
- Fork prong
- Explosion that fails to occur
- Hoot with derision
- Unit of gravitational force
- Agitate
- Plead
- Annoyance
- Plant also known as the windflower
- Lyrical poem

244

Basic level of a subject taken in school	Fluid-filled sac	Cotton fabric with a shiny finish	◣	Country, capital Nairobi	Assistants	Twist into a state of deformity	◣	Nudges
◣	▼	▼		Highly excited	◣	▼		
Jerking								Gammon
Pigpen	◣			Move with great haste	◣			▼
◣							Direct	
Cooking utensil	Herbi-vorous lizard of tropical America		Any leafy plants eaten as vegetables	Oracle	◣		▼	
◣	▼		▼	▼	Close violently	Hire		Covered with lather
Bands of metal worn on the fingers		Domains	◣			▼		▼
◣				Branch of the British armed forces (inits)		Shoddy or tasteless articles		
Fruit pulp		Mistakes	◣	▼		▼		
◣				In the quickest time (abbr)	◣			
Privy to (coll) (2,2)		Protection	◣					

248

Tobacco product	▼	Greatest possible degree	Collection of objects laid on top of each other	▼	Component parts of a skeleton	Embryonic frog	▼	Region regularly afflicted by monsoons
Goods bought from a foreign country ►	▼		▼			▼		Tinted
Obtain something desirable ►					Economic assistance ►			▼
Spindle ►					Division of a week ►			
►					Hurl		Biblical character	
Sheds tears	Emblem		Dread	Chilly ►	▼		▼	
Large shaggy-haired brown bison ►	▼		▼					Brush
►				Becomes firm ►				▼
Reached a destination		Consume food	Common name for the English hawthorn			Seize, appropriate	Epoch	
Microbe ►	▼		▼		Stinging insect ►	▼	▼	
►		Conscious of ►						
Green vegetable	Plaything ►				Breach ►			

Fast discharge of a gun (5,4)		Projecting edge of a roof		Animal with two feet	Former unit of money in Italy		Light and insubstantial (poetic)	
Essential		Allude to		Artful	Chair		Amy Winehouse hit of 2007	
Creep						Mortification, humiliation		One dozenth
Four-winged insect	Run off	Racing vessel						
		Hideout	Melt					
Canvas receptacle from which a horse can feed		Fill to satisfaction		George ___, footballer who died in 2005	Shortened forename of US president Lincoln			
							Astern	
Section of glass					Branch of the British armed forces (inits)			
			Budge					
Stake	Young newt				To the ___ degree (to the utmost)			

247

Ali ___, fictional character	▼	In a murderous frenzy	Cobbler's stand	▼	Expression of surprise or mild alarm	▼	As a result of this	Distributes, deals out
Gifted, competent ▶	▼		▼		Conclusion ▶			▼
Wide-mouthed cup ▶							Fragrant resin used as incense ▼	
▶			Exclamation expressing disgust	Snake-like fish ▶			▼	
Paddles	Short hairs left unshaven ▶		▼					
Quaggy	Arm of the Mediterranean	Withdraw from an organisation		Aye ▶				
▶	▼	▼				Danger		Recipient of money
To stretch out ▶			Waterless	Apple seed ▶		▼		▼
Not in any circumstances		Coffee shop ▶	▼				Unspecified quantity	
▶				Fish with enlarged wing-like fins ▶			▼	
Not married		Godlike ▶						
▶				Strong washing solution ▶				

251

Rope	Spoken	Hydro-phobia	▼	Authori-tative pro-clamation	Instru-ments used for smoothing or shaping	Harden to	▼	Prevents from speaking out
└	▼	▼		Italian car manu-facturer ►		▼		
Part of a barrier or fence ►								Tit for ___
The alphabet (inits) ►				Erotic desire ►				▼
┌							Terminate	
Slide unobtru-sively	Shorebird with slender upward-curving bill		Demesne	English flower, also a girl's name	►		▼	
┌	▼		▼	▼	Love ___, a chair for two	Sharp part of a knife		Time of life between the ages of 13-19
Light-beam amplifier		Frozen dessert made with fruit juice ►				▼		▼
┌					Legendary bird		"It is", poetically	
Typefaces		Supply or impreg-nate with oxygen ►			▼		▼	
┌				Norse deity ►				
Drum	Quantity much larger than is needed ►							

249

Explosive powder, usually in strings	▼	Uncon-scious state	Unit of type, used in printing	▼	Walk unsteadily	▼	Military hat with a flat circular top and a peak	Forename of golfer, Mr Woosnam
⌐					▼		Bird associated with the Tower of London	▼
Dog with a spotted coat		Grazing land	Coconut meat	▶			▼	
⌐		▼						
Person who uses insincere praise	Unwanted discharge of a fluid		Casual tops (1-6)	Adolescent		Vitamin important in vision and bone growth		Taking a break
⌐	▼		▼	▼		▼		▼
Swim for pleasure		Calm, with no emotional agitation	▶					
⌐					Pouches		Portico or roofed colonnade	
Equitable		Assert to be true			▼		▼	
⌐				Opposed	▶			
Makes damp		Business leader	▶					
⌐				Stony waste matter	▶			

253

250

Person who shoes horses	▼	Live-action film about a piglet	Digestive juice secreted by the liver	▼	Posing no difficulty	▼	Painting, sculpture, music, etc	Plot of ground in which plants grow
◣					▼		English river	▼
Unhappy		Tap lightly	Espresso coffee with milk	▶			▼	
◣								
On the move	Figure		Popular chilled beverage (4,3)	Angling pole		Burned remains		Droop
◣	▼		▼	▼	Beast of burden	▶		▼
Assigned to a station		Cheats, swindles	▶				Frequently	
◣					Domestic swine	▶	▼	
Bump into		Cathedral city		Bellow	▼	School group (inits)		Collection
◣		▼		Chooses	▶		▼	▼
Asian plant widely cultivated for its oily beans	Beneficiary of a will	▶						
◣				Harangue	▶			

254

Device providing access to a computer	▼	Bump into	▼	Angling imple-ments	▼	Course of existence / Title given to a nun	▼	Rented out
►		▼				▼		Fastener with a threaded shank
Learn by heart / Crimson	►			Sudden attacks / Has sight of	►			▼
Muddles	►			▼			Horse breed	
►			Rubbed		Pitch	►	▼	
Success-ful stroke in an athletic contest		Uncom-promising in discipline	▼ ►					
►					Uncooked	►		
Heavy open wagons		Woody plant		Hitherto	► ▼	Alone		Flower-pollinating insects
Plug in the mouth of a bottle	Voice qualities / Bird of prey	► ▼				▼	Free	▼
►	▼			Ripped	►		▼	
Shed tears / Shed blood	►			Be prostrate	►			
►				Deities	►			

Persistence of a sound after its source has gone		Mortal		Go out with		Ripened reproductive body of a plant		Cloaks
President of a board of directors								
Temporary military shelter				Russian emperor		Former Portuguese province in China		Closes
Once in a while	Pixie		Secret store					
						Killer whale		Change direction abruptly
Japanese samurai		Academic test (abbr)	Cook in an oven					
				Angry disputes				
Peak	Demented		View	Offspring		English river		Slippery fish
Slaughter								
					Reverential salutation			
Engraving or carving in relief		White substance covering the crown of a tooth						

256

253

Punctuation mark	▼	Jumped over	Other than what is under consideration	▼	Give a sign of welcome	Cry weakly or softly	▼	Action performed intentionally
Frighten (as with threats) ▶	▼					▼		French word for 'black'
Composed of men or boys ▶				Egg-laying fowl ▶				▼
Ponder ▶				Artificial language, a simplification of Esperanto ▶				
⚑				Not in good health		Canton in the centre of Switzerland ▼		
Gentleman's gentleman	Body	US city known for gambling and easy divorce	Branch line ▶	▼		▼		
Type of hunting dog ▶	▼		▼					Brass instrument without valves
⚑			Baby's bed ▶					▼
Portend	Plant with flowers used in brewing		Secure with a wooden pin		Coaster	Pastry dish		
Retail establishment ▶	▼		▼	Measure of fuel used compared to distance covered ▶	▼	▼		
⚑		Electronic message ▶						
Show displeasure vocally	Breed of dog ▶			Quoits target ▶				

254

Indidually, separately	Guarantee	Contended in rivalry	▼	Rudder	▼	Bounders, scoundrels	▼	Attaches with gum or paste
▼	▼	▼						
Nought ►				Film starring Bette Davis, 'All about ___'		Fine net used for veils		Capital of Morocco
Academic term ►				▼		▼		▼
►			Muscular weakness caused by nerve damage		Large nation (inits) ►			
Sprout		Toll of a bell	▼				Railway locomotive	
►				Augment	Meadow ►		▼	
Catherine ___ Jones, actress	Come to earth	Not long before the present ►		▼				
►	▼				University degree (inits)	Male offspring		Where the sun shines and stars twinkle!
Glossy	Invasion by pathogenic bacteria ►			▼	▼		▼	
►				Cry of a goose ►				
Opposed		Chief port of Australia ►						

255

Hindu class / Veteran soldier	▼	Adult male chicken	Master of ceremonies	▼	Plenty	Cut-price events	▼ Prefix meaning a million
▼		▼			▼		Bloc
Smut from a fire ▶					Khan, Islamic religious leader ▶		▼
Fling ▶					Casual ▶		
▶			Spray can	Killed		Former French gold or silver coin	
Jape	Emblem	Donkeys ▶	▼	▼		▼	
Chamfer ▶	▼				Explosion		Cramp
▶			Picture puzzle ▶		▼		▼
Exclude		Units (1/6 inch) used in printing	Bird which hoots ▶			Large brownish-green New Zealand parrot	
Units of force associated with gravity ▶		▼		Alias (inits) ▶		▼	
▶			Fertile desert areas ▶				
Precious stone	volatile, smelling salts	▶		Woollen cap of Scottish origin ▶			

256

Wild cat of Africa	Approximation of quantity, degree or worth	Loads		Bar of metal	Bear	'Key ___', 1948 film starring Bogart and Bacall		Diameter of a tube or gun barrel
				Pigswill				
Heavenly body also known as Sirius								Form of address to a man
Former name of Tokyo, Japan				Greek god of war				
							Kimono sash	
Bringing to a stop	Astonished		One who leaves to live abroad	Make new				
					Room access	Clay pigment		Goes along at great speed
Weapon that delivers an electric shock		Record of events from a personal viewpoint						
					Police investigator of crimes (abbr)		___ and outs, details of a situation	
Fanatical	Characterised by gloom and mystery							
				Sea eagle				
Carry	Overabundance							

257

Former name of Japan's capital city	▼	Period of office of a chief monk	▼	Area surrounding the hole on a golf course	▼	Emotional wound	▼	Humorous anecdote or remark
Place in which photographs are developed	▼							
▼				Chart		Ointment		Wood nymph
Part of the ear	Filled with bewilderment	▼		▼		▼		▼
Central American republic	▼						Earnest	
Eye sore	One score and ten		Condition marked by uncontrollable tremor	▼			▼	
▼	▼		▼	T S ___, British poet	By means of	▼		
Boundary		Belonging to me		Bow	▼			
▼		▼			Joan of ___, French heroine	Primitive fish with long jaws		Stitch
Brazilian port, ___ de Janeiro	▼			Matures	▼	▼		▼
Explosive compound (inits) Stain	▼			Uncommon				
▼			Propeller with several angled blades	▼				

Solutions

1

	P			R		J		L
B	O	M	B	E		E	R	A
	L			C	A	T		W
D	O	L	L	Y		S	K	Y
		A		C	R	A	N	E
J	A	M		L		M	A	R
	S	E	V	E	N		C	
	C		E			S	K	I
R	E	C	E	I	P	T		T
	N	O	R	M		E	T	A
I	T	S		A	V	A	I	L
		H	A	M		K	E	Y

2

	F		R		P		A	
G	U	M	A	R	A	B	I	C
	N	A	N		L	I	R	A
I	N	N	K	E	E	P	E	R
	E		I	G	N	O	R	E
C	L	A	N	G	E	D		T
		L	E	S	S		P	
L	E	I			S	L	O	P
	L	A	C	E		H	O	E
W	A	S	H	B	O	A	R	D
	T		A	B	U	S	E	R
H	E	A	T		T	A	R	O

3

	P		O		T		T	
W	A	R	D	R	O	B	E	
	R	E	D		P	U	N	T
	A	S	S	E	S	S		E
A	F	T		E		H	O	P
	F		S	L	E	E	V	E
H	I	G	H	S		L	I	E
	N		E		G		D	
		S	A	L	A	D		N
D	U	C	T		M	I	C	A
	S	O	H	O		R	I	G
F	E	T	E		P	E	A	S

4

	P		D		B		O	
F	A	M	I	L	I	A	R	
	R	A	G		A	S	B	O
	A	S	S	E	S	S		B
A	N	T		W		A	P	E
	O		S	E	R	I	E	S
A	I	R	E	R		L	E	E
	D		C		C		K	
		T	R	E	A	T		B
T	W	E	E		P	A	P	A
	H	A	T	E		C	A	R
C	O	T	E		B	O	R	E

5

	D		A		P		N	
W	A	R	D	R	O	B	E	
	Y	E	A		L	A	D	Y
	D	A	M	S	O	N		E
A	R	M		C		D	A	M
	E		P	O	L	I	C	E
Y	A	C	H	T		T	I	N
	M		O		I		D	
		B	E	A	N	O		C
T	O	R	N		K	O	H	L
	R	A	I	D		Z	O	O
I	B	E	X		L	E	W	D

6

	B			R		A		
C	U	R	E	A	L	L		H
	R			R	U	M	B	A
U	N	I	V	E	R	S	A	L
		O			K		D	
M	A	N	S	E		E	E	K
	M		T	A	L	E		I
B	O	W	E	R		L	T	D
	U		P		V		I	
I	R	I	S		E	O	N	S
		N	O	M	I	N	E	E
B	O	N	N		L	E	S	T

Solutions

7

	P			B			M		
	U	R	D	U		C	O	B	
	P	E	R	G	O	L	A		
P	A	R	A			A	N	T	
	U	S	E	R	S			O	
P	A	N	T	S		P	E	T	
		I	C	E		K			
E	R	I	C	A		K	E	G	
	I			P	I	E		Y	
	M	A	L	I		T	A	P	
M	E	N		S	E	C	T	S	
		D	I	M		H	E	Y	

8

	B		S		A		A	
R	E	C	O	M	M	E	N	D
	C		N	I	P		T	
C	O	L	I	C		A	L	P
	M		C	A	R	R	E	L
P	E	A			H	I	R	E
		B	A	B	E	L		A
N	A	U	S	E	A		R	
		S	P	A		B	I	B
S	H	E	I	K		O	V	A
	U		R	E	G	R	E	T
S	E	W	E	R		N	T	H

9

	I		S		M		L	
	R	Y	E		A	B	E	L
	R	A	T		G		G	
N	E	P	H	R	I	T	I	S
	M			O		R	O	W
	E	B	B	S		A	N	A
	D	A	R	E		W		N
V	I	N	E		A	L	M	S
	A		A	F	T		A	
	B	A	D		S	I	L	O
	L		T	H	E	M	E	D
M	E	S	H		A	P	S	E

10

	E		P			C		
	S	W	I	T	C	H		B
S	P	A	T		A	I	D	A
		T	H	I	N	N	E	R
J	O	E	Y		V		T	
		R		C	A	F	E	S
	C	Y	N	O	S	U	R	E
	U			V		G	M	T
V	E	R	T	E	X		I	
	S	O	A	R		A	N	A
		D	R	E	A	D	E	D
B	L	E	E	D		O	D	D

11

	C			N		B		
V	I	S	C	E	R	A		G
	T		W	A	S	T	E	
J	E	T	S	T	R	E	A	M
		W			E		K	
S	C	O	P	E		B	E	G
	R		A	G	U	E		E
M	E	T	R	O		D	O	T
	P		T		B		S	
M	E	A	N		A	S	I	F
		L	E	G	A	T	E	E
E	M	I	R		L	Y	R	E

12

	M		A			T		
	A	S	P	I	R	E		D
C	O	O	P		A	N	T	E
		F	L	A	T	T	E	N
M	U	T	E		I		A	
		E		P	O	S	S	E
	U	N	L	I	S	T	E	D
	N			K		R		I
M	I	N	C	E	M	E	A	T
	T	A	O		E	T	U	I
		A	N	N	A	T	T	O
F	I	N	S		L	O	O	N

Solutions

13

	N		O		V		L	
	A	M	B	R	O	S	I	A
	T	A	O		C		N	
S	O	M	E	T	I	M	E	S
		B		A	F	I	R	E
	L	O	O	S	E	N		P
	O			K	R	O	N	A
E	T	C	H		O	R	A	L
		O			U		P	
G	R	A	N	D	S	L	A	M
	E	T	U	I		A	L	E
	D	I	N	E		G	M	T

14

	O		B		G		B	
	D	A	R	K	R	O	O	M
I	D	L	E		E		A	
	B	E	N	E	A	T	H	
	H	I	D	I	N	G		O
	N		P	S	A	L	M	
A	V	O	W		P	I	E	
	I		H		H	E	N	S
E	A	R	E	D			S	
	B	A	R		A	L	E	S
	L	I	E		P	E	E	P
E	E	N		W	E	E	D	Y

15

	L		B			H	
	A	C	T	U	A	T	E
	T	R	A	M		R	A	N
	H	E	L	P		A	L	E
B	E	A	C	H		C		W
		T			T	H	U	S
	S	O	L	D	I	E	R	
P	A	R	A		R	A	N	T
	L		P		E		E
	S	A	S	H		B	U	N
F	A	N		A	M	A	S	S
		T	U	G		T	E	E

16

	S			W		O		N
	P	O	O	H		U	S	E
	U	P	R	O	O	T		A
I	D	E	S			S	E	T
		R	O	S	E	T	T	E
		A		Y		R	U	N
A	T	T	E	N	D	E	D	
	R	E	N	O		T	E	N
	Y		E	P	I	C		A
H	O	U	R	S		H	O	P
	U		G	I	V	E	U	P
S	T	A	Y	S		D	R	Y

17

		I		R		U		L
A	R	R	A	Y		N	A	E
		I		D	E	A	L	T
W	A	S	T	E		W	I	G
	L		U	R	S	A		O
F	L	A	N		I	R	A	
		P		C	R	E	S	S
C	O	P	R	A		S	K	I
	C	O	A	T	I			L
R	E	I	N	S	T	A	T	E
	A	N	T		C	L	A	N
T	N	T		C	H	A	N	T

18

	A		J		A		C	
	G	R	A	N	U	L	A	R
	A	I	M		G		V	
F	R	E	S	H	E	N	E	R
		L		A	R	O	S	E
A	S	S	E	T		H		E
	K			S	T	O	C	K
B	I	N	D		A	W	A	Y
	E			I		S		
	B	A	S	E	L	E	S	S
B	A	T	I	K		V	I	A
	D		R	E	V	E	A	L

Solutions

19

	B		C		M		E	
	A	B	O	V	E	P	A	R
	L	I	P		N		V	
S	I	D	E	L	I	N	E	D
		E		A	N	I	S	E
	A	S	S	I	G	N		F
	B			D	I	N	G	O
D	E	F	T		T	Y	R	E
		L			I		I	
C	H	O	R	I	S	T	E	R
	I	R	A	N		E	V	E
	P	A	W	N		N	E	T

20

		D		B		P		A
C	H	A	I	R		I	W	O
		I		I	N	N	E	R
A	R	S	O	N		P	E	T
	Y		P	E	S	O		A
M	E	L	T		K	I	D	
		A		S	I	N	U	S
C	A	R	T	E		T	O	T
	S	C	A	N	T			R
S	P	E	C	T	A	C	L	E
	I	N	K		P	A	S	S
I	C	Y		B	E	N	D	S

21

	B		A		G			D
	A	R	G	U	A	B	L	E
S	T	A	R		Z			M
		B	E	C	A	U	S	E
A	B	B	E	Y		K	I	N
		I		C	H	A	R	T
N	A	T		L		S		I
	V		P	E	S	E	T	A
M	A	G	I		U		R	
	T		P	A	M	P	A	S
B	A	B	E	L		E	Y	E
	R		S	P	A	R	S	E

22

			G				A	
A	C	H	E		S	M	U	G
	R	A	C	Q	U	E	T	
	E	L	K		P	L	O	Y
D	E	V	O	T	E	E		A
		E			R	E	E	K
B	A	S	T	E			R	
	V		O	L	D	H	A	T
B	O	O	T	S		A		U
	W		T	E	R	R	O	R
H	A	K	E		U	S	A	F
	L		R	I	G	H	T	S

23

	A		F			G		B
	S	Y	R	A	C	U	S	E
	T	O	E			L		R
F	R	U	S	T	R	A	T	E
	A		C	A	U	G	H	T
C	Y	B	O	R	G		E	
		E		I	S	L	E	T
S	H	E	A	F		E		S
	O	L	D	F	L	A	M	E
A	R	I	D		A	D	I	T
	S	N	E	E	R	E	R	S
B	E	E	R		K	N	E	E

24

			S			M		
T	E	R	N		B	L	A	G
	N	E	U	T	R	A	L	
	I	M	F		A	V	I	D
E	D	I	F	I	C	E		I
		S			T	R	I	M
O	A	S	I	S			O	
	M		S	O	D	I	U	M
B	U	I	L	T		N		E
	L		A	S	P	E	C	T
W	E	A	N		A	R	I	A
	T		D	E	N	T	A	L

Solutions

25

		E				N		
S	A	C	S		O	N	U	S
	B	A	S	T	I	O	N	
	E	R	A		L	O	S	T
P	L	A	Y	P	E	N		O
		F			D	E	B	T
C	R	E	E	K			O	
	E		S	E	D	A	T	E
H	A	S	T	Y		D		V
	D		A	S	H	O	R	E
P	E	A	T		I	R	O	N
	R		E	X	P	E	C	T

26

		B		A		C		A
G	L	A	N	D		H	A	G
		R		I	M	A	G	O
P	O	S	S	E		R	A	N
	V		T	U	B	A		Y
L	A	C	Y		A	D	O	
		L		S	H	E	A	F
S	P	A	D	E		S	K	I
	I	R	O	N	Y			N
E	X	I	S	T	E	N	C	E
	I	T	S		T	E	A	R
F	E	Y		D	I	T	T	Y

27

	H			O		F		A
L	U	C	I	D		O	A	P
	L	A	N	D	A	U		O
M	A	R	C			R	E	G
		C	H	O	R	T	L	E
		A		V		H	U	E
L	E	S	S	E	N	E	D	
	S	E	E	R		S	E	W
	C		P	S	S	T		H
B	U	T	T	E		A	B	E
	D		E	A	S	T	E	R
G	O	A	T	S		E	Y	E

28

	S			I			P	
T	S	U	N	A	M	I		
	E	A	R	N		E	L	F
	E	N	G	E	N	D	E	R
O	R	D	E	R		I		E
		B			I	C	E	S
	C	A	B		N	I	G	H
H	A	R	A	S	S		O	
	C		N		T	A	T	S
	T	I	A	M	A	R	I	A
K	I	L	N		N	E	S	T
	L	A	C	T	A	T	E	

29

		B				I		
S	T	R	A	N	G	E	R	
	H	I	D		R	U	I	N
A	I	M			A	L	S	O
	R		R	E	D	O		W
I	D	L	E		U	G	L	I
		C	R	A	Y	O	N	
	S		E		T		B	
R	O	A	D	B	E	D		A
	A	V	E	R		A	R	C
S	K	I		A	S	T	O	R
		D	I	N		A	W	E

30

	G		A		E		T	
	A	C	A	D	E	M	Y	
	S	O	M	E		U	P	S
	P	A	M	P	H	L	E	T
A	S	C	O	T		L		O
		H			W	E	A	R
	R	E	P		A	R	U	M
M	E	D	A	L	S		S	
	M		E		T	A	T	E
	I	L	L	F	A	T	E	D
E	T	A	L		G	O	R	E
	C	A	V	E	M	E	N	

Solutions

31

```
. F . A . D . G .
B R A S S E R I E
. E L K . T E A R
D E T E R R I N G
. Z E D . O N T O
P E R . H I S . T
. C O A T . H . .
C H A T S . P A N
. O T T . P O L O
O R I E L . L O O
. D O R Y . K E N
F E N . E R A S E
```

32

```
. P . F . . H .
. A S K A N C E
. S P I T . L I D
. T I N T . E R A
M A N G Y . A . D
. D . . O N T O
. S L O B B E R
K E E N . O R Y X
T . Y . E . . Y
. T A X I . A L L
S O S . F U G U E
. H A S . A G M
```

33

```
. S . A . . P . Z
S T I M U L A T E
. Y . B . . C . U
S E V E N S E A S
. S E R U M . L .
. . A . M U F T I
V E L V E T E E N
. L . . R . A R T
S U N D A E S . E
. D A U B . T O G
L E G A L . E W E
. S L E N D E R
```

34

```
. . U . D . O .
E N U N C I A T E
. U R I . V . H
. A N T E A T E R
E N S . V . I R A
. C . G A L L . T
T E L L . . D U E
. . A P P E N D
T O R S O . . W
. N . S E C R E T
K Y L E . H U L A
. X . S H I E L D
```

35

```
. D . . G . . B .
. A L M O N E R
. N E O N . A I M
. C A R E F R E E
D E F E R . W . T
. . L . . T I D E
. P E G . A G E S
C I T R U S . F .
. E . E . T U R F
. C R E D I T O R
L E O N . N A S A
. W E I G H T Y
```

36

```
. . . A . . . B .
A C E S . D R O P
. U N C L E A R
U S E R . S I N K
. T . I B I S . I
G A R B . R E D S
. R . E R O D E S
. D . . . U . S
U P H O L S T E R
. I O W A . S R I
N E V E R . A T M
. E N D O R S E
```

Solutions

37

		C			M			
K	E	N	O		D	R	E	W
	V	E	R	S	I	O	N	
K	E	E	N		S	T	U	N
	R		C	O	D	A		A
T	Y	R	O		A	T	O	P
	W		B	R	I	E	F	S
	H				N		F	
N	E	C	E	S	S	A	R	Y
	R	O	T	E		G	O	A
P	E	A	C	E		R	A	W
		T	H	R	E	A	D	S

38

	P		C		S			
	Y	A	H	W	E	H		O
C	A	P	E		N	O	U	N
		A	C	E	T	O	N	E
B	A	C	K		A		C	
		H		A	I	R	E	S
	H	E	A	D	L	I	N	E
	E			V		B	S	E
D	R	Y	D	E	N		O	
	B	O	O	R		E	R	E
		G	O	T	E	V	E	N
F	E	A	R	S		A	D	D

39

		R		D		S		F
A	B	I	D	E		H	E	R
		C		B	R	A	V	O
A	B	H	O	R		N	A	G
	R		F	A	S	T		S
M	A	T	T		H	I	S	
	A		W	E	E	K	S	
I	S	T	L	E		S	I	T
	U		T	I	L	E		O
S	A	I	N	T	P	A	U	L
	V	E	T		E	I	R	E
P	E	R		F	E	R	N	S

40

	P		P		R		L	
	E	C	O	N	O	M	I	C
	R	U	M		B		B	
S	U	R	P	R	I	S	E	S
		V		U	N	C	L	E
G	E	E	S	E		R		A
	L			S	P	A	S	M
O	M	S	K		S	P	A	Y
		W			S		I	
	T	A	L	L	T	A	L	E
C	A	N	O	E		C	O	G
	B		B	O	L	E	R	O

41

	B		D		D		D	
S	E	P	A	R	A	T	E	D
	R	E	T		T		M	
	E	L	E	V	A	T	O	R
V	A	T		I		A	B	E
	V		F	E	N	S		B
H	E	R	O			T	H	E
		R	E	P	E	A	L	
O	W	L	E	T			T	
	E		S	A	H	A	R	A
D	A	M	E		O	W	E	S
	K		E	M	E	N	D	S

42

	Y		B		B		C	
	O	P	E	R	A	T	O	R
	Y	E	N		C		R	
M	O	O	T	P	O	I	N	T
		N		E	N	N	U	I
	T	Y	K	E		F		T
	E			K	N	E	E	L
C	A	R	D		E	R	N	E
		E			W		T	
S	H	A	R	K	S	K	I	N
	U	R	E	A		E	R	A
E	S	P	Y		N	E	B	

Solutions

43

	C			C			H	
T	O	R	T	O	I	S	E	
	P	O	U	R		A	R	C
	R	U	C	K		L	O	O
H	A	N	K			S		C
		D		K	N	A	C	K
	J	U	L	I	E		A	
C	U	P		B	A	N	N	S
	N			B	R	A		I
	T	O	F	U		S	O	L
R	A	F		T	H	A	N	K
		F	E	Z		L	O	Y

44

	O		I		C		I	
S	P	A	N	I	A	R	D	S
	T	I	T		T	O	O	T
T	I	M	E	T	A	B	L	E
	O		R	A	C	I	S	M
A	N	D	I	R	O	N		S
		I	M	A	M		L	
H	R	S			B	A	A	L
	E	C	R	U		M	B	A
O	B	S	E	S	S	I	O	N
	E		L	E	A	G	U	E
F	L	A	Y		T	O	R	S

45

	C			E		A		B
	O	A	F	S		T	A	R
	K	I	R	S	C	H		A
H	E	R	A			L	B	W
		D	U	D	G	E	O	N
		R		I		T	R	Y
W	O	O	D	S	M	E	N	
	E	P	I	C		S	E	A
	D		G	R	A	F		G
L	E	V	E	E		O	A	R
	M		S	T	R	O	D	E
H	A	S	T	E		T	O	E

46

	C		W		B		U	
H	O	T	E	L	I	E	R	
	R	O	D		L	Y	N	X
	R	U	S	T	L	E		R
B	I	T		E		L	E	A
	D		E	X	P	I	R	Y
C	O	U	N	T		D	O	S
	R		M		L		S	
		S	A	L	E	S		M
W	E	T	S		D	A	T	A
	M	A	S	K		V	A	N
L	U	G	E		G	E	N	E

47

	L			C			B	
	O	R	B	I	T	A	L	
	S	U	E	T		M	U	D
	E	N	V	Y		I	R	E
B	R	A	Y			S		N
		W		D	U	S	T	Y
	P	A	P	E	R		O	
B	A	Y		S	A	L	T	Y
	S			P	L	Y		E
	T	A	X	I		R	Y	A
W	A	R		S	K	I	E	R
		T	E	E		C	A	N

48

	C		S		D		R	
	A	P	P	R	O	V	A	L
	G	O	A		U		J	
H	E	A	R	T	B	E	A	T
		C		A	L	P	H	A
	C	H	O	R	E	S		K
	U		A	B	O	D	E	
H	E	A	R		A	M	E	N
		G			S		S	
A	F	O	R	E	S	A	I	D
	O	R	A	L		C	R	U
	B	A	N	K		T	E	E

Solutions

49

	C			R		P		H
B	A	D	G	E		E	W	E
	F			I	A	N		A
T	E	R	M	S		P	E	P
		E		S	C	A	R	E
U	S	E		U		L	A	D
	P	L	I	E	D		S	
	L		M			K	E	G
R	I	V	A	L	R	Y		E
	C	A	M	E		O	W	N
H	E	M		A	F	T	E	R
		P	A	P		O	N	E

50

			P		L		A	
F	I	B	O	N	A	C	C	I
	D	O	S		T		T	
	I	N	T	R	E	P	I	D
J	O	N	A	H		I	V	Y
	C		G	O	S	P	E	L
H	Y	D	E		E			A
			S	E	A	S	O	N
B	A	N	T	A	M		L	
	P		A	R	M	A	D	A
G	E	R	M		A	R	I	D
	D		P	A	N	T	E	D

51

	L		R		M		D	
F	A	C	E		I	C	E	D
	P	U	B		S	O	F	A
A	T	T	E	N	T	I	O	N
	O		C	O	R	N	E	T
S	P	E	C	I	E	S		E
		T	A	R	A		A	
L	A	H			T	H	I	S
	R	O	B	E		O	R	C
R	O	S	E	W	A	T	E	R
	M		R	E	V	E	R	E
B	A	N	G		E	L	S	E

52

	V		G		F		R	
	O	P	E	R	A	T	O	R
	T	O	R		U		O	
T	E	R	M	I	N	A	T	E
		C		B	A	L	S	A
	T	H	A	I		G		R
	O		S	C	A	L	E	
A	M	M	O		R	E	A	D
		A		E		T		
C	A	N	D	L	E	L	I	T
	G	L	U	E		O	N	E
	E	Y	E	D		T	O	G

53

	W		A		D		U	
	R	E	V	E	R	E	N	D
	E	W	E		I		P	
E	N	E	R	G	E	T	I	C
		R		A	R	E	N	A
	U	S	S	R		E		C
	F			B	A	T	C	H
B	O	L	D		G	H	E	E
		A			U		R	
D	I	S	C	R	E	D	I	T
	A	S	B	O		U	S	E
	N	O	S	E		B	E	E

54

	W			L				P
	E	P	H	E	M	E	R	A
	I	R	I	S		C		P
B	R	I	M	S	T	O	N	E
		O			A	L	A	R
	G	R	A	P	H	I	C	S
	R		I		I		H	
V	I	B	R	A	T	I	O	N
	P	O	P	L	I	N		O
	P	O	O	L		D	U	N
M	E	T	R	E		I	R	E
	D		T	Y	R	A	N	T

Solutions

55

	L			L		C		F
N	O	R	M	A		O	R	E
	N	I	A	C	I	N		N
K	E	N	T			T	U	N
	G	E	N	U	I	N	E	
	L		A			N	I	L
C	L	E	A	R	C	U	T	
	O	T	I	C		A	Y	E
	D		R	O	O	T		X
A	G	N	E	S		I	C	E
	E		R	I	G	O	U	R
B	R	A	S	S		N	E	T

56

	J		M		W		S	
	O	M	E	L	E	T	T	E
	H	A	T		A		I	
U	N	S	E	T	T	L	E	D
		A		W	H	O	S	E
	M	I	L	I	E	U		A
	O			G	R	I	L	L
B	O	O	R		I	S	I	S
		P			N		M	
W	O	E	B	E	G	O	N	E
	D	R	A	G		N	E	B
	D	A	D	O		O	R	B

57

	A		B		N		S	
	P	R	E	T	E	N	C	E
	S	H	E		C		R	
D	E	E	P	F	R	I	E	D
		I		L	O	N	E	R
	E	N	R	A	P	T		O
	L			K	O	R	A	N
B	L	A	B		L	O	R	E
		R			I		N	
S	H	E	E	P	S	K	I	N
	O	N	C	E		I	C	E
	T	A	U	T		T	A	T

58

			F				I	
C	A	B	L	E	C	A	R	
	L	A	Y		O	R	A	L
B	I	T			M	A	N	Y
	V		T	O	M	B		O
M	E	G	A		E	L	A	N
			S	T	R	E	S	S
	N		S		C		K	
N	O	T	E	L	E	T		O
	R	O	L	E		R	A	M
M	A	O		S	T	A	G	E
		L	I	T		P	A	N

59

	W			O		O		S
B	A	B	E	L		L	A	P
	S	O	R	D	I	D		U
T	H	U	G			W	A	R
		D	O	C	K	I	N	G
		O		O		V	I	E
S	C	I	E	N	C	E	S	
	A	R	M	S		S	E	T
	S		B	U	S	T		R
S	T	O	R	M		A	H	A
	R		Y	E	L	L	O	W
D	O	N	O	R		E	E	L

60

	S			D			H	
	C	A	L	Y	P	S	O	
	A	M	O	K		E	B	B
	R	A	R	E		C	O	O
M	E	L	D	S		R		A
		G			B	E	S	T
	C	A	N	T	A	T	A	
T	O	M	E		N	E	W	S
S		A		E				A
	T	A	P	S		C	R	Y
D	A	N		L	O	U	I	S
		D	A	Y		T	O	O

271

Solutions

61

	G			L		F			
F	A	R	R	A	G	O		A	
	Z			P	R	O	W	L	
B	A	C	K	P	E	D	A	L	
	O			W		R			
B	O	B	B	Y		H	R	S	
	N		R	E	V	I	E	W	
S	I	N	E	W		D	N	A	
	O		A		B			G	
K	N	O	T		I	T	E	M	
		C	H	O	L	E	R	A	
A	N	T	E		E	A	R	N	

62

			B		U		O		
A	R	B	I	T	R	A	R	Y	
	E	A	R		A		D		
	S	H	O	U	L	D	E	R	
N	I	T		S		O	R	E	
	D		H	E	A	D		I	
M	E	T	E			G	I	N	
		A	T	H	E	N	S		
P	A	N	D	A			C		
	L		S	T	R	A	I	T	
B	L	U	E			O	N	T	O
	Y		T	A	N	D	E	M	

63

			C				S		
E	T	C	H		S	M	U	G	
	H	O	O	D	L	U	M		
	E	R	R		A	L	O	E	
U	N	N	E	R	V	E		M	
		E			E	S	A	U	
C	H	A	P	S			L		
	E		R	A	B	B	I	T	
D	E	F	O	G		E		E	
	D		M	A	D	A	M	E	
J	E	E	P		I	R	O	N	
	D		T	H	E	S	I	S	

64

	C			A		T		I	
	O	B	I	T		R	I	M	
	C	A	M	E	R	A		A	
O	K	R	A			N	A	G	
		I	M	P	A	S	S	E	
		S		L		C	I	D	
S	I	T	U	A	T	E	D		
	R	A	P	T		N	E	E	
	O		D	Y	E	D		L	
U	N	C	A	P		E	D	O	
	I		T	U	R	N	U	P	
A	C	H	E	S		T	O	E	

65

	D			D			F		
	R	E	L	A	P	S	E		
	A	T	O	M		P	A	P	
	M	E	A	N		E	T	A	
C	A	R	D	S		C		C	
	N			S	I	D	E		
	P	A	S	S	K	E	Y		
W	A	L	K		U	S	E	D	
	S		I		A			O	
	T	E	S	T		H	A	Y	
F	A	R		A	L	I	K	E	
	R	A	M		M	A	N		

66

		L		A		T		S	
P	I	O	U	S		R	A	T	
		K		P	L	A	C	E	
B	L	I	N	I		N	E	W	
	A		A	C	T	S		S	
S	W	A	B		E	M	S		
		N		A	D	I	O	S	
C	H	O	U	X		T	U	T	
	A	U	G	E	R			A	
B	R	I	L	L	I	A	N	T	
	E	L	Y		C	L	U	E	
A	S	H		M	E	L	T	S	

Solutions

67

		R				N		
N	I	N	A		V	I	A	L
	N	E	S	T	I	N	G	
	T	A	P		C	U	S	P
C	O	R	S	A	I	R		O
	L			O	N	C	E	
G	O	Y	A		U		U	
	N		C	O	S	S	E	T
C	E	L	E	B		H		R
	W		T	I	R	A	D	E
N	A	Z	I		A	R	I	A
	Y		C	E	M	E	N	T

68

			H				S	
C	A	M	E		P	A	I	D
	S	O	A	K	I	N	G	
S	P	A	T		P	I	N	T
	H		I	T	E	M		A
C	Y	A	N		L	U	C	K
	X		G	E	I	S	H	A
	I			N		A		
R	A	S	P	B	E	R	R	Y
	T	O	L	L		A	L	E
D	E	F	O	E		T	E	N
	A	D	D	R	E	S	S	

69

	B		S			E		
	E	S	T	E	E	M		B
S	T	A	R		M	I	C	E
		L	I	B	E	R	A	L
D	I	V	A		T		G	
		I		W	I	R	E	D
	M	A	G	I	C	E	Y	E
	A			G		S		G
E	X	P	O	S	I	T	O	R
	I	O	N		R	O	U	E
		R	E	M	O	R	S	E
A	R	T	S		N	E	T	S

70

	H			H		V		
M	A	N	D	E	L	A		C
	T			L	A	S	S	O
B	E	D	S	P	R	E	A	D
	O			D		L		
A	L	T	I	M	E	T	E	R
	E		M	O	R	O	S	E
T	E	M	P	O		M		V
	W		A	R	A	B	L	E
L	A	S	S		H	O	U	R
	R		S	H	E	L	L	S
E	D	G	E		M	A	L	E

71

	B		R		V		O	
W	E	R	E	W	O	L	F	
	D	E	N		L	E	F	T
	L	A	D	I	E	S		A
A	I	L		C		S	E	X
	N		R	E	V	E	R	E
F	E	T	I	D		R	O	D
	N		P		T		S	
		B	O	W	E	L		S
W	O	E	S		D	O	T	E
	B	A	T	H		V	I	N
D	I	R	E		S	E	E	D

72

	C		R		B		S	
F	A	C	E	S	A	V	E	R
	N		N	A	N		R	
C	A	B	E	R		T	I	P
	P		W	I	T	H	E	R
L	E	U			R	U	S	E
		S	T	I	E	S		P
D	E	A	R	M	E		C	
	G	A	P			C	O	B
A	R	E	N	A		O	V	A
	O		C	I	N	D	E	R
D	E	F	E	R		A	Y	E

Solutions

73

		R				R		
A	U	R	A		S	H	A	M
	R	A	C	C	O	O	N	
	A	V	E		B	R	I	G
A	L	A	R	M	E	D		A
		G			R	E	E	L
C	R	E	S	T			M	
	E		H	I	C	C	U	P
B	A	T	O	N		H		A
	M		R	E	P	A	I	R
L	E	F	T		T	R	O	T
	R		S	T	A	T	U	S

74

			D				F	
S	P	L	I	T	P	E	A	.
	A	I	M		E	M	I	T
B	Y	E			D	I	R	E
	E		S	W	I	G		S
B	E	E	P		G	R	I	T
		R	A	R	E	L	Y	
	F		I		E		K	
F	I	F	T	E	E	N		B
	J	O	E	Y		A	P	R
B	I	N		E	L	I	T	E
	D	A	D		L	A	W	

75

	T		S		N		K	
	O	R	T	H	O	D	O	X
	F	E	E		T		R	
S	U	R	P	R	I	S	E	S
		U		O	C	E	A	N
	U	N	I	T	E	D		O
	Z			E	A	G	E	R
D	I	M	E		B	E	N	T
		U			L		G	
C	A	N	D	L	E	L	I	T
	B	R	I	E		I	N	N
	C	O	M	A		P	E	T

76

	M		T		B		D	
	P	R	I	S	O	N	E	R
T	H	E	M		L		L	
	N	E	M	E	S	I	S	
	R	E	S	O	R	T		W
		G		M	O	O	S	E
C	H	E	F			V	I	A
	O		I		K	E	N	T
S	O	B	E	R			C	
	P	U	N		W	R	E	N
	L	S	D		E	U	R	O
H	A	T		E	B	B	E	D

77

			C				B	
T	U	B	E		R	E	E	D
	T	O	L	U	E	N	E	
	A	L	L		V	E	N	T
T	H	E	O	R	E	M		O
		R			N	A	A	N
T	H	O	U		U		P	
	O		S	I	E	R	R	A
M	O	P	E	D		A		H
	K		N	A	T	I	V	E
J	A	N	E		A	S	I	A
	H		T	H	R	E	A	D

78

	M			T		M		
M	A	R	Q	U	E	E		G
	L			F	A	R	C	E
M	I	D	S	T	R	E	A	M
		O			L		R	
F	A	N	C	Y		A	T	M
	B		H	A	I	R		O
T	O	T	E	M		K	I	P
	D		D		M		N	
R	E	A	D		A	B	L	E
		L	A	M	P	R	E	Y
W	E	I	R		S	A	T	E

Solutions

79

	B			B		L		
M	O	M	B	A	S	A		D
	D			S	L	I	C	E
E	Y	E	S	H	A	D	O	W
		C			B		H	
A	B	U	S	E		B	O	W
	L		E	R	G	O		O
G	U	L	A	G		A	D	O
	R		W		A		I	
I	S	L	E		L	O	C	O
		B	E	L	A	T	E	D
L	E	W	D		S	T	Y	E

80

		V				R		
C	O	M	A		R	H	E	A
	B	A	L	L	O	O	N	
	O	N	E		U	N	T	O
D	E	N	T	A	T	E		U
		E			E	D	I	T
M	E	R	C	Y			R	
	L		R	E	U	S	E	S
B	E	F	I	T		C		C
	V		S	I	L	A	G	E
W	E	E	P		E	L	A	N
	N		S	A	D	D	L	E

81

			A			D		
C	O	P	S		B	L	U	R
	P	A	Y	L	O	A	D	
	A	L	E		S	T	E	M
F	L	A	T	O	U	T		A
		T			N	E	A	T
B	E	E	C	H			I	
		D	R	I	P	P	L	E
H	I	V	E	S		H		G
		T	A	S	H	O	R	E
B	O	S	S		O	N	U	S
		R	E	X	T	E	N	T

82

	B		S		C		A	
	O	S	C	U	L	A	T	E
	A	H	A		O		T	
P	R	O	B	O	S	C	I	S
		V		P	E	R	C	H
M	E	D	U	S	A			A
O				S	H	I	R	K
T	B	A	R		A	G	U	E
	Z				V		S	
S	O	U	T	H	E	A	S	T
A	R	I	A			P	I	E
F	E	E	D			T	A	N

83

	B		B			A		E
S	A	T	I	S	F	I	E	D
	L		T			D		G
E	L	S	E	W	H	E	R	E
	S	U	S	H	I		I	
		R		Y	E	A	S	T
O	D	E			D	U	K	E
	R		B			D	Y	E
S	A	M	U	R	A	I		N
	M	E	S	A		B	R	A
B	A	T		G	U	L	A	G
		E	N	E		E	W	E

84

	T		V		H		G	
B	I	L	E		A	W	E	S
	E	A	R	P	H	O	N	E
	I	N	S		A	R	E	A
S	N	E	E	R		S		W
				O	B	E	S	E
H	I	S		D	A	N	T	E
	S	T	R	E	S	S	E	D
O	R	E	O	S			L	
	P	O	S	S	I	B	L	E
	O	P	T		S	O	A	K
A	D	S		S	T	A	R	E

Solutions

85

		L				B		
M	U	S	E		H	A	U	L
	R	E	A	D	I	L	Y	
	G	A	S		D	A	S	H
W	E	A	T	H	E	R		A
	I			O	M	I	T	
L	I	R	A		U		K	
	S		R	U	S	S	E	T
S	L	U	R	P		W		R
	A		E	S	T	A	T	E
I	N	K	S		O	T	I	S
	D		T	I	G	H	T	S

86

	L		H		C		C	
	A	R	I	A		O	U	R
	M	A	D	D	E	N		I
C	A	G	E			S	I	N
		T	A	S	T	I	N	G
		I		U		D	U	E
P	O	M	A	N	D	E	R	
	H	E	R	B		R	E	F
	D		R	A	T	A		I
B	E	R	E	T		B	B	C
	A		S	H	I	L	O	H
B	R	U	T	E		Y	O	U

87

		S				J		
T	A	P	E		W	R	A	P
	C	A	N	T	E	E	N	
	M	U	D		A	B	E	D
C	E	N	S	U	R	E		O
	C				I	L	L	S
A	C	H	E		E		E	
	A		G	U	S	S	E	T
S	T	A	R	R		N		R
	N		E	N	C	A	S	E
B	A	R	S		O	P	E	N
	P		S	E	N	S	E	D

88

	O		H		A		C	
	A	C	M	E		T	E	A
	H	A	I	R	D	O		T
N	U	T	S			M	I	N
		S	T	A	M	I	N	A
		E		N		C	E	P
J	O	Y	R	I	D	E	R	
	B	E	A	M		N	T	H
	L		V	A	L	E		Y
C	A	R	A	T		R	P	M
	T		G	O	R	G	O	N
W	E	B	E	R		Y	E	S

89

	H		C			G		
	O	C	A	R	I	N	A	
	M	A	N	E		O	L	D
	E	R	O	S		M	A	R
G	R	A	N	T		I		A
		V			G	N	A	W
	B	A	R	R	I	E	R	
L	I	N	O		R	E	E	F
	R		U		L			A
	T	A	X	I		O	W	L
O	H	M		C	H	A	O	S
		P	A	Y		F	E	E

90

		H		B		A		C
L	H	A	S	A		B	R	A
		L		L	U	R	I	D
C	E	L	L	S		A	P	E
	E		O	A	K	S		T
C	L	E	G		O	I	L	
		X		D	I	V	E	R
K	H	A	K	I		E	Y	E
	A	M	I	S	S			C
P	R	I	N	C	I	P	L	E
	E	N	D		L	A	O	S
U	S	E		P	O	R	T	S

Solutions

91

	U			O		S		
	G	N	A	T		I	M	F
	L	A	C	I	N	G		E
K	Y	O	T	O		N	O	W
		M		S			P	
	L	I	C	E	N	S	E	D
	O		A		H	I	R	E
B	A	R	N		S	C	A	N
	T	O	O	L		K		
	H	O	N	E		P	I	G
W	E	T		A	P	A	C	E
		S	I	N		Y	E	T

92

	J			H		S		
B	A	N	Q	U	E	T		V
	D			G	R	O	P	E
P	E	P	P	E	R	P	O	T
		E			S		G	
O	K	A	P	I		J	O	Y
	Y		O	R	S	O		A
E	L	O	P	E		G	Y	P
	I		U		E		A	
D	E	A	L		C	O	R	E
		V	A	G	R	A	N	T
A	V	E	R		U	R	S	A

93

	C		M			C		B
T	A	R	A	N	T	U	L	A
	K		O			B		I
M	E	R	R	I	M	E	N	T
	S	H	I	R	E		I	
	E		A	M	B	E	R	
V	I	A			O	U	C	H
	M		B			L	E	I
L	A	T	E	R	A	L		Z
	G	A	L	A		I	D	O
B	O	P		G	L	O	O	M
		E	K	E		N	E	E

94

		V				P	
L	A	T	E		S	N	A	G
	B	A	R	R	I	E	R	
	L	I	D		S	W	A	B
H	E	L	I	C	A	L		Y
	O			L	Y	R	E	
S	T	R	I	P		U		
	R		C	A	C	H	E	T
B	I	K	E	R		E		A
	V		B	E	F	A	L	L
L	I	M	A		O	V	A	L
	A		G	R	E	E	D	Y

95

	L			W		B		
	I	S	L	E		A	S	K
	M	A	I	D	E	N		I
L	O	T	S			K	I	T
		S	T	U	D	E	N	T
		U		Z		R	A	Y
A	R	M	P	I	T		N	
	E	A	R			S	E	T
	P		E	L	S	E		O
R	E	C	T	O		P	A	N
	A		T	A	X	I	N	G
L	L	O	Y	D		A	D	S

96

	R			B		S		
R	A	T	R	A	C	E		V
	Z			G	A	M	M	A
R	E	C	E	S	S	I	O	N
		O			H		V	
E	P	O	C	H		S	E	A
	H		A	I	D	A		Y
D	O	U	B	T		W	A	R
	N		I		M		G	
B	E	A	N		A	U	R	A
		D	E	N	I	Z	E	N
S	H	O	T		D	I	E	T

Solutions

97

	F			P			M	
	A	S	K	A	N	C	E	
	T	I	L	L		A	N	D
	A	D	A	M		B	U	D
G	L	E	N	S		I		A
		C			O	N	L	Y
	M	A	R	Q	U	E	E	
C	U	R	E		S	T	A	Y
	M		A		T			E
	P	U	M	A		M	O	A
A	S	S		R	E	A	D	S
		E	E	K		D	D	T

98

	C		K		A		L	
S	A	G	A		S	T	O	W
	C	A	R	R	I	A	G	E
	H	I	M		A	B	E	T
G	E	T	A	T		A		N
				I	S	S	U	E
H	E	R		P	A	C	K	S
	V	I	R	T	U	O	U	S
	A	D	I	O	S		L	
	D	E	C	E	A	S	E	D
	E	R	E		G	A	L	A
A	D	S		S	E	W	E	D

99

	C			D			F	
	H	O	S	A	N	N	A	
	L	A	U	D		A	R	M
	O	R	E	S		C	O	O
W	E	S	T			R		A
		M		T	W	E	E	T
	C	A	M	E	O		V	
C	O	N		M	O	L	A	R
	A			P	L	Y		O
	C	A	P	E		R	A	W
C	H	I		S	P	I	K	E
		M	O	T		C	A	D

100

			G		A		C	
C	O	C	H	I	N	E	A	L
	R	U	E		T		R	
	P	R	E	M	I	S	E	S
S	H	E		O		A	S	P
	A		C	O	A	T		E
I	N	F	O			I	R	A
			V	E	N	E	E	R
C	A	G	E	Y			S	
	V		R	E	M	A	I	N
R	O	M	E		A	C	N	E
	W		D	E	T	E	S	T

101

	M		B			T		
	P	A	R	I	A	H		B
A	G	R	A		B	O	M	B
		B	I	V	O	U	A	C
G	O	O	D		A		S	
		U		I	R	A	T	E
	B	R	A	N	D	N	E	W
	E			F		A	R	E
C	R	I	T	I	C		M	
	G	R	I	D		R	I	B
	A	N	E	M	O	N	E	
V	I	N	Y	L		D	D	T

102

	R		E		O		S	
	I	C	O	N		N	O	W
	S	L	U	D	G	E		E
F	E	E	T			S	O	D
	A	S	C	R	I	B	E	
	N		A		D	E	N	
R	E	S	E	R	V	E	S	
	Z	E	R	O		D	E	W
	I		R	U	I	N		E
I	N	C	A	S		E	L	L
	E		T	E	A	S	E	D
U	S	U	A	L		S	O	S

278

Solutions

103

	A			B			S	
	R	I	S	O	T	T	O	
	O	R	A	L		A	S	S
	M	O	L	E		B	O	W
V	A	N	E			O		A
		A		M	O	O	D	Y
	O	G	R	E	S		I	
A	P	E		S	L	A	N	T
	E			S	O	T		I
	R	I	G	A		L	A	P
D	A	M		G	L	A	S	S
		P	O	E		S	H	Y

104

		N		B		C		
D	E	T	O	N	A	T	O	R
	R	O	E		T		M	
	M	O	L	A	S	S	E	S
N	I	L		L		U	S	E
	N		P	L	U	S		D
F	E	T	A			H	U	G
			R	A	V	I	N	E
R	E	L	A	X			W	
	L		P	E	S	T	E	R
D	A	M	E		O	I	L	Y
	N		T	A	N	G	L	E

105

		H				B	
O	G	R	E		S	C	A	M
	E	A	R	M	A	R	K	
	N	I	B		D	I	E	S
L	E	S	S	O	N	S		E
		I			E	P	E	E
B	A	N	D		S		N	
	N		E	R	S	A	T	Z
W	I	L	C	O		T	H	E
	M		A	B	S	O	R	B
B	A	L	M		A	L	A	R
	L		P	A	E	L	L	A

106

		L				B	
A	R	M	Y		R	U	E	D
	E	A	R	N	E	S	T	
	A	N	I		B	U	S	T
T	R	A	C	T	O	R		O
		G			U	P	T	O
S	T	E	P		N		O	
	I		R	I	D	E	R	S
O	P	T	I	C		X		C
	T		M	Y	O	P	I	A
B	O	D	E		W	E	L	L
	E		D	O	L	L	O	P

107

	B			H		T		S
M	A	C	H	O		R	A	M
	B	A	U	B	L	E		I
S	A	N	G			S	O	L
		T	H	E	A	T	R	E
		A		M		L	A	Y
O	C	T	U	P	L	E	T	
	O	A	T	H		T	E	G
	P		T	A	K	A		E
C	I	T	E	S		B	O	O
	E		R	I	F	L	E	D
B	R	A	S	S		E	R	E

108

	N		F		W		S	
B	E	V	E	R	A	G	E	
	W	E	E		D	O	C	K
	C	A	S	S	I	S		Y
C	O	L		A		S	A	L
	M		B	I	K	I	N	I
F	E	R	A	L		P	O	E
	R		T		R		N	
		S	H	E	E	P		D
H	O	L	E		D	O	S	E
	D	A	R	E		L	O	B
B	E	T	S		B	O	U	T

Solutions

109

		S			H		
P	I	T	H		P	H	E	W
	D	R	A	G	O	O	N
	L	O	W		S	O	S	O
N	E	O	L	I	T	H		R
		P			S	A	L	T
E	A	S	E	L			E
	P		C	O	R	S	E	T
L	I	S	Z	T		P		E
	A		E	S	C	A	P	E
B	R	I	M		A	R	U	M
	Y		A	B	B	E	S	S

110

	M		P		M		D
C	O	P	E		A	T	O	M
	C	O	N	C	R	E	T	E
	H	E	N		S	L	E	D
L	A	M	I	A		A		D
			R	E	V	E	L
C	B	S		D	R	I	V	E
	O	N	C	E	O	V	E	R
	W	E	A	N	S		R
	S	E	N	T	I	N	E	L
	E	R	E		V	A	S	E
H	R	S		L	E	N	T	O

111

	A		A			T	
	S	T	R	A	F	E		B
S	P	U	R		R	E	A	R
	C	A	N	A	S	T	A
I	N	K	Y		C		T
	E		H	A	L	A	L
	T	R	E	A	S	U	R	E
	H		L		C		O
D	I	S	H	O	N	E	S	T
	S	A	E		A	R	I	A
	S	E	M	I	N	A	R
K	O	H	L		L	E	N	D

112

		D			F	
F	I	L	E		G	I	L	L
	S	O	M	E	O	N	E
	I	O	U		D	D	A	Y
A	S	T	R	I	D	E		A
	E			E	X	A	M
W	A	D	I		S		C
	S		C	O	S	S	E	T
A	T	S	E	A		I		H
	R		C	R	A	D	L	E
M	A	M	A		R	E	A	R
	L		P	L	E	D	G	E

113

	C		D		B		F
S	H	O	E	M	A	K	E	R
	E	B	B		T	O	R	I
R	E	S	I	S	T	A	N	T
	S	E	T		E	L	S	E
P	E	R		I	R	A		S
	V	E	R	Y		A
S	L	A	V	E		A	R	C
	A	T	E		L	O	G	O
B	R	I	N	K		R	U	M
	V	O	T	E		T	E	E
S	A	N		Y	E	A	S	T

114

	D		Y		M		B
D	E	C	O	R	A	T	E
	F	O	G		L	E	T	S
	E	R	A	S	E	S		T
F	A	N		U		T	W	O
	T		S	C	R	E	E	N
D	E	A	T	H		D	A	Y
	D		R		A		R
	S	E	E	D	S		B
M	O	L	E		D	A	T	A
	W	I	T	H		M	A	T
A	N	T	S		P	E	N	S

Solutions

115

	P		C		U			
	H	A	R	L	O	T		W
G	I	L	A		C	A	F	E
		K	I	T	C	H	E	N
B	R	A	G		U		R	
		L		P	L	U	M	E
	M	I	N	S	T	R	E	L
	A			A		I	N	K
I	T	S	E	L	F		T	
	S	O	R	T		Z	I	P
		A	N	E	M	O	N	E
C	A	P	E	R		E	G	G

116

	A			W		D		
L	U	M	B	A	G	O		L
	R			S	O	L	V	E
R	A	N	G		W	E	E	K
	U			N		R		
P	A	N	E	L		A	Y	E
	G		S	I	N	G		L
F	O	R	C	E		A	S	K
	R		A		C		P	
L	A	P	P		O	W	E	D
		H	E	A	T	H	E	N
N	U	D	E		S	O	D	A

117

	A		O		F			
	P	E	T	R	O	L		H
B	E	N	T		R	O	B	E
	R	E	D	D	E	E	R	
S	C	A	R		E		D	
	G			C	A	D	R	E
	P	E	C	U	L	I	A	R
	L			R		E	G	G
N	E	U	T	E	R		G	
	A	R	E	A		A	L	P
	G	A	L	I	L	E	O	
D	W	E	L	L		A	D	D

118

	S		P			L		
	C	A	R	O	U	S	E	
	O	N	U	S		A	G	A
	U	N	I	T		T	O	G
S	T	U	N	S		S		U
	L			D	U	P	E	
	S	A	R	C	O	M	A	
M	E	R	E		R	A	N	G
T		I		A				R
	T	A	N	G		S	E	E
M	O	P		A	B	O	V	E
	T	A	P		Y	E	N	

119

		G				C		
H	O	P	I		C	O	A	L
	G	I	Z	Z	A	R	D	
	R	P	M		B	A	S	H
D	E	P	O	S	I	T		O
	I			N	E	W	T	
S	A	N	T	A			A	
	F		E	N	R	A	G	E
F	L	Y	N	N		D		X
	O		N	E	G	A	T	E
T	A	X	I		A	G	A	R
	T		S	I	L	E	N	T

120

	O			H		B		
	G	C	S	E		A	W	L
	R	E	P	A	I	R		Y
B	E	R	Y	L		B	S	E
	E		E			U		
	E	S	P	R	E	S	S	O
L		A			S	P	A	R
D	E	M	I		P	A	N	T
	V	E	R	B		T		
	E	A	S	E		I	O	U
I	N	N		G	N	A	W	S
		S	O	S		L	E	A

Solutions

121

		H				L		
S	O	S	O		L	O	I	N
	V	A	R	I	O	U	S	
	A	I	D		S	T	A	R
A	L	L	E	G	E	D		A
		O			R	O	A	N
L	A	R	G	E			N	
	G		A	L	W	A	Y	S
N	E	E	D	S		R		L
	O		G	E	N	E	R	A
A	L	O	E		A	N	O	N
	D		T	E	N	A	N	T

122

	B		O			U		
	R	E	C	A	P	S		B
C	A	R	T		A	S	H	Y
		R	E	F	E	R	E	E
B	E	A	T		L		A	
		N		S	L	A	V	E
	S	T	R	E	A	K	E	R
	U		R		A	N	A	
B	E	H	A	V	E		S	
	T	A	X	I		V	E	G
		R	E	C	L	I	N	E
A	M	P	L	E		A	T	E

123

		F					F	
U	S	S	R		C	A	L	F
	A	L	A	B	A	M	A	
	K	I	N		L	O	N	E
L	I	N	C	O	L	N		V
	K			O	G	L	E	
B	A	S	S		U		A	
	C		E	N	S	I	G	N
J	U	D	E	A		D		O
	M		S	P	R	E	A	D
B	E	T	A		N	A	P	E
	N		W	H	A	L	E	S

124

	R			P		G		
	I	S	L	E		A	C	E
	C	O	O	P	E	R		M
C	E	P	S			R	E	M
		R	E	L	I	E	V	E
		A		O		T	O	T
B	A	N	G	O	R		K	
	S	O	L			L	E	D
	T		A	P	S	E		A
R	H	I	N	O		P	O	T
	M		C	O	H	E	R	E
P	A	P	E	R		R	E	D

125

	I			C			H	
	M	A	H	A	T	M	A	
	A	M	E	N		O	H	M
	G	U	S	T		S	A	E
L	E	S	S			E		T
		I		W	A	S	T	E
	A	N	N	E	X		A	
B	U	G		S	L	A	N	T
	D			T	E	D		I
	I	S	L	E		O	W	N
E	T	A		R	U	P	E	E
		C	A	N		T	E	A

126

	E		F		T		U	
	P	R	O	F	O	U	N	D
	I	O	N		T		P	
S	C	A	T	T	E	R	E	D
		S		A	M	I	G	O
	S	T	E	P		F		O
	I			S	O	L	A	R
S	T	A	B		N	E	W	S
		Z			U		H	
C	O	U	R	T	S	H	I	P
	F	R	A	U		A	L	A
	T	E	N	T		Y	E	W

Solutions

127

		M			B		
N	O	V	A		G	R	E	W
	B	A	S	S	O	O	N	
	E	C	O		O	D	D	S
C	Y	A	N	I	D	E		I
	N				S	O	O	T
N	O	T	E	D			A	
	U		Y	A	C	H	T	S
E	T	H	E	R		E		T
	W		L	E	G	A	T	E
F	I	N	E		A	T	O	M
	T		T	I	G	H	T	S

128

	L		O		O		C	
	I	M	P		R	O	U	T
	V	A	T		A		R	
S	E	N	S	E	L	E	S	S
	R			T		L	E	T
	S	P	A	N		A	D	O
	A	I	D	A		T		U
F	U	N	D		T	E	S	T
	S		R	Y	E		H	
	A	X	E		X	R	A	Y
	G		S	T	A	P	L	E
D	E	N	S		S	M	E	W

129

	T		L		D		N	
S	A	L	A	C	I	O	U	S
	N		P	O	P		T	
A	N	N	U	L		A	M	P
	O		P	A	R	C	E	L
G	Y	M			U	R	G	E
		A	S	I	D	E		A
S	E	R	E	N	E		M	
		E	C	U		P	E	N
L	A	S	E	R		A	L	E
	I		D	E	G	R	E	E
A	D	D	E	D		T	E	D

130

	S		N			N		A
P	H	N	O	M	P	E	N	H
	E		V			W		O
C	A	M	E	R	A	S	H	Y
	R	E	L	A	X		Y	
		S		P	I	P	E	S
A	S	S			S	A	N	E
	H		A			R	A	G
F	I	L	C	H	E	S		M
	R	I	T	A		N	E	E
G	E	M		C	A	I	R	N
	O	A	K		P	A	T	

131

	E			B		H		
	R	E	E	L		E	M	S
	G	A	R	A	G	E		E
T	O	G	A	S		L	O	T
		E		T			A	
	T	R	E	S	P	A	S	S
	E		A		I	D	E	A
D	E	B	T		G	A	S	P
	T	R	E	E		P		
	H	A	N	S		T	E	A
Y	E	W		P	L	O	Y	S
		N	A	Y		R	E	P

132

	L		E		D		B	
	I	N	I	M	I	C	A	L
	O	A	R		S		B	
U	N	S	E	T	T	L	E	D
		T		A	R	I	S	E
	S	Y	S	T	E	M		F
	E			A	S	I	D	E
B	A	S	E		S	T	I	R
		H			E		R	
P	R	A	N	K	S	T	E	R
	A	L	O	E		E	L	Y
	T	E	R	N		D	Y	E

Solutions

133

	P		C		L		G	
R	E	C	O	V	E	R	Y	
	R	O	T		N	U	M	B
	S	W	E	A	T	S		A
C	O	L		W		T	A	G
	N		C	A	S	I	N	G
C	A	R	R	Y		C	O	Y
	L		U		P		N	
		H	I	V	E	S		L
A	L	A	S		P	O	L	O
	I	T	E	M		L	O	B
P	E	E	R		C	O	P	E

134

			B				K	
S	O	D	A		A	C	E	D
	M	A	S	O	N	R	Y	
	E	N	S		G	I	S	T
U	N	C	O	I	L	S		A
	E				O	P	E	N
R	U	D	E	R			A	
	N		M	A	R	A	U	D
W	A	D	E	R		L		E
	B		R	E	T	I	N	A
B	L	O	G		A	V	O	N
	E		E	G	R	E	S	S

135

	B		B					T
	E	A	R		D	U	L	Y
	A	B	A	C	U	S		R
P	R	A	Y		M	A	L	E
		S			B		E	
	P	E	R	C	E	I	V	E
	I		E	A	R	L		N
A	T	O	L	L		L	A	D
	F		E	L	K		G	
M	A	C	A	O		E	R	E
	L		S	U	R	R	E	Y
B	L	U	E	S		G	E	E

136

	P		S		S		O	
F	A	R	M	Y	A	R	D	
	L	E	U		R	U	D	E
	P	A	T	O	I	S		M
L	A	M		M		S	A	C
	B		S	I	M	I	L	E
A	L	L	O	T		A	G	E
	E		M		C		A	
		M	E	D	I	C		T
P	O	O	H		A	L	S	O
	A	L	O	T		A	R	E
B	R	E	W		A	M	I	D

137

	A		P			S		
	S	T	A	R	C	H		D
S	K	I	D		L	I	D	O
	T	R	A	I	N	E	E	
A	N	T	E		N		G	
	E		M	I	T	R	E	
	P	R	E	A	C	H	E	R
	R		D		Y	E	A	
S	O	F	T	E	N			S
	P	E	R	I		F	L	U
	T	E	R	R	I	E	R	
O	S	A	K	A		B	E	E

138

	D			W		R		
L	A	C	T	A	T	E		M
	T			K	O	A	L	A
P	E	P	P	E	R	P	O	T
		I				Y		P
O	M	E	G	A		S	E	A
	A		A	R	C	O		I
S	C	O	T	T		P	O	D
	O		E		D		F	
G	N	A	W		R	O	T	A
		P	A	L	A	V	E	R
P	R	E	Y		Y	A	N	K

Solutions

139

	S		D			A		R
	C	H	A	R	I	S	M	A
	A	I	R			P		V
A	R	M	I	S	T	I	C	E
	C		N	I	A	C	I	N
L	E	D	G	E	R		T	
	R		S	A	T	Y	R	
I	N	A	P	T		H		I
	A	G	R	A	R	I	A	N
D	U	N	E		O	R	B	S
	R	E	S	E	T	T	L	E
N	U	T	S		E	Y	E	D

140

	R			C		Z		
T	O	R	N	A	D	O		O
	T			P	A	N	D	A
L	A	W	N		W	E	E	K
		H			N		M	
S	C	O	O	P		Z	I	P
	A		V	I	C	E		Y
C	R	E	E	P		D	N	A
	V		R		B		O	
F	E	E	S		O	T	T	O
		L	E	A	T	H	E	R
S	A	F	E		H	Y	D	E

141

	W		T			K		
	H	E	A	R	S	E		Y
L	Y	N	X		T	Y	K	E
		D	E	P	O	S	I	T
W	E	E	D		A		W	
		A		S	T	O	I	C
	B	R	O	W	S	E		U
	L		E		R	I	D	
B	A	N	T	E	R		R	
	B	E	A	T		R	A	Y
	E	L	E	V	A	T	E	
L	A	D	E	N		F	E	W

142

	O		F		B			F
	F	A	L	S	E	T	T	O
A	F	R	O		S			I
		T	E	X	T	U	R	E
D	A	I	S	Y		P	U	G
		S		L	E	P	E	R
A	N	T		E		E		A
	U		S	M	A	R	T	S
B	R	I	E		L		E	
	S		P	O	L	A	N	D
F	E	T	I	D		W	O	O
	D		A	D	H	E	R	E

143

			D				F	
O	N	C	E		B	A	I	T
	E	A	S	T	E	R	N	
	A	S	K		N	O	S	E
C	R	U	S	H	E	S		A
		A			F	E	L	T
P	U	L	P		I		Y	
	N		L	A	T	T	E	R
F	I	N	A	L		R		E
	Q		C	L	E	A	N	S
S	U	R	E		R	I	O	T
	E		S	T	A	N	D	S

144

			H				D	
G	A	T	E		I	B	E	X
	V	A	N	I	L	L	A	
	E	O	N		L	E	N	T
A	R	I	A	D	N	E		E
		S			E	D	G	E
L	A	M	P		S		N	
	R		R	E	S	C	U	E
C	A	R	E	S		I		V
	B		S	P	A	R	S	E
G	L	U	E		I	C	O	N
	E		T	Y	R	A	N	T

Solutions

145

	H			L		B		
M	A	S	S	A	G	E		H
	I			C	O	A	T	I
C	L	A	W		O	N	U	S
	K			D		T		
C	L	A	S	P		P	U	P
	I		C	O	T	E		O
I	N	L	E	T		A	R	E
	E		N		C		I	
B	R	A	E		H	E	L	L
	T	R	A	I	N	E	E	
J	O	E	Y		P	E	S	O

146

			K			D		
R	I	P	E		T	A	I	L
	N	A	N	K	I	N	G	
	F	L	Y		M	I	S	T
P	O	L	A	R	I	S		I
		O			D	E	B	T
C	A	R	O	B			O	
	N		V	O	O	D	O	O
M	O	G	U	L		E		W
	I		L	A	W	F	U	L
K	N	E	E		H	O	P	E
	T		S	H	Y	E	S	T

147

	A		O		S			T
	L	A	U	D	A	B	L	E
P	E	R	T		S			N
		R	E	S	H	A	P	E
A	B	I	D	E		M	U	M
		V		L	A	P	S	E
B	E	E		M		L		N
	M		L	A	T	E	S	T
F	I	R	E		U		M	
	G		A	U	T	H	O	R
B	R	A	S	S		A	K	A
	E		E	A	G	L	E	T

148

	S			B			F	
	T	A	P	I	O	C	A	
	A	M	O	K		A	R	T
	L	A	N	E		L	O	W
H	E	L	D			V		I
		G		S	L	E	E	T
	C	A	M	E	O		R	
A	R	M		A	S	S	E	T
	U			B	E	T		O
	M	A	L	I		A	U	K
F	B	I		R	I	N	S	E
	D	A	D		D	E	N	

149

			K		E		B	
R	E	S	E	N	T	F	U	L
	N	A	P		N		S	
	I	N	T	R	A	N	E	T
A	G	E		Y		A	S	H
	M		R	E	N	T		R
B	A	L	E			A	C	E
		O	U	T	L	A	W	
S	C	A	R	S			S	
	H		D	E	C	E	I	T
F	A	K	E		U	L	N	A
	P		R	A	T	I	O	N

150

	W			Y		M		S
	O	B	O	E		I	R	E
	R	E	U	S	E	S		A
W	E	D	S			A	G	M
		R	E	S	I	D	U	E
		O		P		V	I	N
H	E	C	T	O	R	E	D	
	S	K	I	T		N	E	E
	C		S	L	O	T		X
C	U	R	S	E		U	L	T
	D		U	S	U	R	E	R
B	O	X	E	S		E	T	A

Solutions

151

	O		G		N		G	
O	P	T	O	M	E	T	R	Y
	P	E	G		A	R	E	A
C	O	N	G	E	R	E	E	L
	S		L	A	M	E	N	T
N	E	M	E	S	I	S		A
		I	D	E	S		L	
B	I	T			S	C	O	T
	B	E	T	A		L	O	W
A	S	S	O	C	I	A	T	E
	E		D	E	C	R	E	E
I	N	F	O		Y	A	R	D

152

	I		H			G		P
A	D	V	A	N	T	A	G	E
	E		V			V		R
L	A	S	E	R	B	E	A	M
	L	I	N	E	R		L	
		L		B	A	S	I	S
E	L	L			T	U	N	E
	L		A			B	E	G
R	A	N	C	H	E	S		M
	M	O	T	E			I	R	E
N	A	T			R	E	S	I	N
		E	G	O		T	O	T

153

		L		D		S		E
C	H	A	I	R		P	A	N
		V		A	G	E	N	T
C	L	A	I	M		A	T	E
	I		T	A	S	K		R
L	E	S	S		K	I	T	
		W		P	I	N	E	S
G	E	E	S	E		G	A	P
	R	A	T	E	S			E
S	A	T	E	L	L	I	T	E
	S	E	W		A	C	I	D
H	E	R		O	P	E	N	S

154

	C		J		A		B	
P	O	W	E	R	B	O	A	T
	M	O	W		A	N	N	A
P	E	R	E	N	N	I	A	L
	I	L	L		D	O	L	L
E	N	D		S	O	N		Y
	F	A	U	N		P		
G	R	A	S	P		H	E	W
	I	M	P		P	A	R	A
G	O	O	E	Y		S	I	R
	J	U	N	E		T	O	N
W	A	S		N	E	E	D	S

155

	P			C			I	
	A	S	S	U	M	E	D	
	S	T	A	R		L	E	A
	S	A	G	E		D	A	B
K	E	N	O			E		L
	D		F	O	R	G	E	
	O	U	S	E	L		E	
A	M	P		T	I	L	E	S
	E			L	O	O		A
	G	I	R	O		C	O	Y
W	A	R		C	H	A	R	S
	E	L	K		L	E	O	

156

	A		Q			T		B
	N	E	U	T	R	I	N	O
	N	E	O			N		W
C	E	N	T	I	P	E	D	E
	X		E	C	L	A	I	R
L	E	S	S	E	E		D	
		U		A	A	R	O	N
S	P	R	I	G		A		I
	A	M	N	E	S	I	A	C
C	L	I	P		A	N	N	E
	E	S	U	R	I	E	N	T
F	R	E	T		D	D	A	Y

287

Solutions

157

		F		D		C		
M	E	D	I	C	I	N	A	L
	M	U	G		E		M	
	B	E	S	O	T	T	E	D
O	R	T		W		A	L	A
	Y		C	E	P	S		U
G	O	Y	A			T	U	N
		R	E	P	E	N	T	
A	Z	T	E	C			L	
	E		F	O	S	S	I	L
G	U	R	U		O	A	K	S
	S		L	A	N	D	E	D

158

			G				A	
N	A	S	A		M	U	S	H
	M	A	F	I	O	S	I	
	E	L	F		T	U	F	T
A	N	A	E	M	I	A		A
		M			F	L	A	X
P	O	I	L	U			W	
	R		A	N	N	A	L	S
F	I	E	N	D		L		H
	G		C	O	R	O	N	A
A	I	D	E		E	N	I	D
	N		T	I	M	E	L	Y

159

		M				P		
G	A	L	A		S	A	R	I
	C	O	N	C	E	D	E	
	H	U	G		R	I	P	S
R	E	V	E	R	I	E		O
	R			O	U	C	H	
B	E	E	B		U		O	
	M		U	P	S	H	O	T
P	E	N	N	E		Y		U
	T		Y	A	P	P	E	R
F	I	J	I		Y	E	L	P
	C		P	E	A	R	L	S

160

		B				E		
E	A	R	L		P	U	R	E
	N	E	A	R	I	N	G	
	T	A	N		L	I	S	A
P	I	C	C	O	L	O		S
		T			I	N	C	H
V	I	S	A		O		H	
	C		B	U	N	Y	I	P
D	E	B	U	G		O		A
	C		S	H	A	D	O	W
E	A	S	E		W	E	R	E
	P		R	E	E	L	E	D

161

	V			S		R		C
D	E	M	U	R		E	G	O
	T	A	R	I	F	F		A
D	O	S	E			R	E	X
	C	A	P	T	I	V	E	
	A		R		G	A	D	
B	U	R	D	E	N	E	D	
	M	A	I	M		R	E	M
	P		V	I	S	A		O
F	I	V	E	S		T	A	P
	R		R	E	M	O	V	E
B	E	A	T	S		R	E	D

162

	B			A			I	
	A	C	I	D		D	D	T
	B	A	R	O	Q	U	E	
J	E	R	K			T	A	D
	A	S	D	I	C			O
M	O	T	O	R		H	A	T
		M	E	N		R		
A	R	I	E	S		A	C	T
	E			S	I	N		W
	E	T	U	I		G	E	E
F	L	U		N	I	E	C	E
	B	A	G		L	O	T	

Solutions

163

	U		B		D		B	
	N	O	T	E		I	D	O
	D	U	R	E	S	S		U
L	O	T	I			C	A	R
	C	O	N	J	O	I	N	
	R		E		U	S	E	
S	H	O	W	G	I	R	L	
	O	P	A	L		T	E	A
	O		N	I	C	E		R
S	P	R	I	G		O	A	R
	L		N	E	B	U	L	A
B	A	D	G	E		S	P	Y

164

	W			P		C		F
T	A	B	L	E		O	N	O
	N	E	U	R	O	N		R
W	E	L	L			N	A	G
		O	U	T	S	I	D	E
		V		U		N	I	T
P	R	E	S	T	I	G	E	
	I	D	L	E		T	U	B
	Y		O	L	I	O		A
T	A	M	P	A		W	A	S
	D		E	G	R	E	S	S
C	H	A	S	E		R	H	O

165

	A			A		J		R
	L	E	N	S		O	W	E
	T	A	I	P	E	I		D
C	O	R	N			N	T	H
		L	E	S	O	T	H	O
		O		C		V	E	T
S	U	B	S	U	M	E	S	
	P	E	E	L		N	E	E
	B		S	P	O	T		R
G	E	T	A	T		U	S	A
	A		M	O	R	R	I	S
E	T	H	E	R		E	N	E

166

	T		A					J
	A	L	B		R	U	L	E
	C	A	L	L	E	R		E
P	O	R	E		S	N	I	P
		G			I		N	
	F	O	L	K	S	O	N	G
	R		U	N	T	O		A
B	I	L	G	E		H	R	S
	T		G	E	M		O	
S	T	R	A	P		A	W	E
	E		G	A	N	D	E	R
A	R	M	E	D		O	R	E

167

	C			O		F		T
G	O	F	A	R		E	V	E
	V	I	C	T	O	R		M
R	E	A	M			M	A	P
		N	E	G	L	E	C	T
		C		A		N	H	S
E	X	E	C	R	A	T	E	
	Y	E	A	R		A	D	D
	L		R	I	F	T		O
B	O	R	I	S		I	C	Y
	S		N	O	M	O	R	E
F	E	I	G	N		N	U	N

168

			U				T	
B	U	L	L		G	R	U	B
	R	A	C	C	O	O	N	
	S	U	E		G	M	A	N
B	A	R	R	A	G	E		A
		E			L	O	A	N
B	U	L	B		E		Y	
	N		R	U	S	S	E	T
B	L	E	E	P		H		A
	O		A	S	S	E	R	T
M	A	S	S		H	E	A	T
	D		T	W	E	N	T	Y

Solutions

169

	P		D			A		
	R	U	I	N	E	D		E
T	O	N	S		N	I	C	E
		S	C	A	T	T	E	R
C	I	A	O		A		N	
		F		V	I	S	T	A
	D	E	V	A	L	U	E	D
	A			L		E	N	D
O	R	P	H	A	N		N	
	K	E	E	N		T	I	G
		E	A	C	H	W	A	Y
T	O	R	T	E		A	L	P

170

	S		B		U		C	
	L	Y	E		G	E	A	R
	E	A	T		L		V	
N	E	P	H	R	I	T	I	S
	P			A		I	A	N
	I	N	S	T		P	R	O
	N	O	U	S		S		R
E	G	G	S		B	Y	T	E
	P		P	A	L		H	
	I	C	E		E	P	I	C
	L		C	A	S	H	E	W
B	L	O	T		S	I	F	T

171

		B		C		K		
R	E	G	U	L	A	T	O	R
	M	A	N		S		R	
	B	I	G	W	H	E	E	L
A	R	T		I		N	A	Y
	Y		A	N	T	S		O
B	O	W	S		U	R	N	
		S	C	R	E	W	S	
M	A	C	A	O		A		
	H		U	N	B	E	N	D
B	E	L	L		U	R	D	U
	M		T	E	T	R	A	D

172

	W		L			M		
	O	T	I	O	S	E		A
J	O	I	N		T	A	R	N
		R	E	L	A	T	E	D
M	E	A	N		I		S	
		D		T	R	E	E	S
	P	E	D	E	S	T	A	L
	I		R		C	R	Y	
C	E	N	T	R	E		C	
	S	O	Y	A		O	H	M
		E	R	I	T	R	E	A
H	E	L	E	N		T	R	Y

173

	H		B		C			
	O	R	C	A		A	D	D
	B	A	R	G	E	S		R
N	O	N	O			S	L	Y
		S	P	A	T	I	A	L
		A		X		S	T	Y
E	C	C	L	E	S		H	
	A	K	A			T	E	A
	L		T	O	G	A		N
G	I	V	E	N		S	E	T
	C		S	U	B	T	L	E
G	O	A	T	S		E	M	S

174

	T		E			P		V
G	A	B	A	R	D	I	N	E
	P		S			T		R
N	E	C	E	S	S	A	R	Y
	R	E	S	E	T		H	
		L		T	O	P	I	C
P	A	L			P	A	N	E
	L		B			R	O	N
V	I	S	A	V	I	S		T
	B	A	D	E		N	O	R
B	I	T		S	K	I	V	E
	E	A	T		P	A	D	

Solutions

175

	P		G		R		G	
	E	S	O	T	E	R	I	C
	S	H	E		A		V	
G	O	O	S	E	S	T	E	P
		N		M	O	A	N	S
	B	E	G	I	N	S		A
	E			R	A	T	E	L
D	E	C	K		B	E	A	M
		E			L		T	
B	L	A	T	H	E	R	E	D
	A	S	I	A		U	R	I
	T	E	N	D		B	Y	E

176

	B		G			S		
	A	D	R	I	F	T		A
K	N	E	E		R	O	M	P
		P	A	R	A	P	E	T
S	H	O	T		C		L	
		S		H	A	L	A	L
	K	E	R	O	S	E	N	E
	Y			U		I	C	Y
P	A	G	O	D	A		H	
	T	A	X	I		B	O	Y
		G	E	N	T	I	L	E
O	M	A	N	I		G	Y	P

177

	L		K		T		B	
	A	N	I	M	A	T	E	D
	M	A	C		N		I	
B	A	C	K	S	T	A	G	E
		R		T	A	M	E	S
	O	E	D	E	M	A		T
	U			P	O	S	S	E
E	T	N	A		U	S	E	R
		O			N		N	
S	L	I	G	H	T	E	S	T
	A	S	I	A		T	O	O
	D	E	N	Y		A	R	M

178

		F		K		S		T
C	R	E	D	O		T	O	O
		L		P	R	A	W	N
V	I	T	A	E		M	E	N
	R		S	K	E	P		E
O	A	F	S		T	E	D	
		U		W	A	D	E	S
F	A	R	C	E		E	W	E
		T	A	L	L			N
S	K	I	N	T	I	G	H	T
	E	V	E		L	I	A	R
A	W	E		P	Y	G	M	Y

179

	E			C			B	
	D	A	D	O		D	O	E
	G	R	I	N	D	E	R	
B	E	G	S			L	E	A
		O	R	B	I	T		G
D	O	N	O	R		A	P	E
			B	U	D		E	
C	A	S	E	S		T	A	G
	L			H	E	R		Y
	T	R	I	O		A	S	P
Y	O	U		F	L	I	E	S
		E	L	F		L	A	Y

180

	K			R		R		C
A	N	G	L	E		A	D	O
	E			F	O	G		L
S	W	I	N	E		T	A	U
		N		R	E	A	L	M
C	A	T		E		G	I	N
	B	O	G	E	Y		B	
	R		O			H	I	D
B	A	N	D	E	A	U		O
	D	I	S	C		M	O	P
Z	E	N		H	E	A	V	E
		E	G	O		N	A	Y

Solutions

181

	K	M			A		P	
A	N	N	O	Y	A	N	C	E
	I		W			T		R
E	F	F	E	C	T	I	V	E
	E	R	R	O	R		E	
		E		N	A	D	I	R
T	W	E	N	T	Y	O	N	E
	E			A		U	S	A
H	A	L	T	I	N	G		C
	V	A	I	N		L	A	H
L	E	V	E	E		A	C	E
		A	R	R	E	S	T	S

182

			P				O	
E	C	R	U		E	S	P	Y
	O	A	T	C	A	K	E	
	O	P	T		V	I	N	E
G	L	I	S	T	E	N		A
		E			S	T	A	R
C	I	R	C	A			L	
	T		R	I	P	P	L	E
B	A	K	E	D		E		V
	L		D	E	B	A	S	E
F	I	J	I		I	R	A	N
	C		T	A	B	L	E	T

183

			F				S	
T	S	A	R		F	A	T	E
	P	L	A	C	E	B	O	
	I		I		R	Y	A	S
A	N	G	L	E	R	S		I
	H				O	M	E	N
C	A	T	S		U		R	
	V		T	A	S	S	E	L
L	A	T	E	X		I		A
	T		R	E	D	E	E	M
T	A	T	E		O	G	R	E
	R		O	T	T	E	R	S

184

	D		T		A		B	
N	I	S	I		C	R	A	G
	A	L	L	T	H	E	R	E
	R	I	D		E	D	D	Y
H	Y	P	E	R		T		S
				E	R	A	S	E
A	S	P		T	A	P	I	R
	P	I	T	I	L	E	S	S
	A	L	O	N	E		T	
	R	E	T	A	I	L	E	R
	S	U	E		G	I	R	O
C	E	P		C	H	E	S	T

185

	G			U		H		
O	A	K	T	R	E	E		C
	L			G	A	R	B	O
D	E	P	R	E	S	S	E	D
	E			T		T		
S	C	A	M	P		P	A	S
	R		A	L	O	E		A
B	A	D	L	Y		G	U	Y
	N		M		W		T	
W	E	B	S		A	L	T	O
		S	E	R	R	I	E	D
G	R	E	Y		P	E	R	E

186

	B			B		T		H
T	I	A	R	A		A	B	E
	T	R	A	D	E	R		I
N	E	S	S			T	O	G
		E	P	I	T	A	P	H
		N		N		R	E	T
W	H	I	S	T	L	E	R	
	A	C	M	E		S	A	D
	V		U	R	E	A		J
H	A	Y	D	N		U	Z	I
	N		G	A	R	C	O	N
N	A	V	E	L		E	O	N

Solutions

187

```
.  C  P  .  .  N  .  F  .
D  A  L  A  I  L  A  M  A
.  S  .  Y  .  .  Z  .  Z
M  E  T  E  O  R  I  T  E
.  S  U  E  D  E  .  A  .
.  .  C  .  D  A  C  H  A
O  A  K  .  .  P  O  O  R
.  G  .  O  .  .  N  E  T
F  A  T  C  A  T  S  .  I
.  V  E  T  S  .  O  R  C
F  E  E  .  B  E  R  Y  L
.  .  M  O  O  .  T  E  E
```

188

```
.  S  .  O  .  O  .  S  .
.  H  A  A  R  .  N  O  W
.  A  L  L  E  G  E  .  E
S  W  A  T  .  .  S  A  D
.  .  M  O  R  A  I  N  E
.  .  O  .  E  .  D  O  N
M  E  D  I  A  T  E  D  .
.  L  E  N  S  .  D  E  C
.  D  .  H  O  R  N  .  H
V  E  G  A  N  .  E  K  E
.  S  .  L  E  S  S  E  E
S  T  E  E  D  .  S  A  P
```

189

```
.  E  .  B  .  .  L  .  S
P  A  R  A  G  R  A  P  H
.  G  .  K  .  .  V  .  O
C  E  L  E  B  R  A  T  E
.  R  A  D  I  O  .  W  .
.  .  C  .  T  O  P  I  C
U  S  E  .  .  F  A  C  E
.  H  .  F  .  .  T  E  N
P  A  C  I  F  I  C  .  T
.  D  A  T  A  .  H  E  R
P  E  R  .  T  H  E  R  E
.  .  D  I  E  .  S  A  D
```

190

```
.  .  .  A  .  .  .  V  .
K  E  P  T  .  O  G  E  E
.  L  A  S  H  O  U  T  .
.  A  T  E  .  Z  I  O  N
U  N  R  A  V  E  L  .  O
.  .  O  .  .  D  E  A  D
A  T  L  A  S  .  .  C  .
.  E  .  C  O  B  W  E  B
B  A  S  E  D  .  I  .  U
.  B  .  T  A  N  N  E  R
S  A  R  I  .  A  G  A  R
.  G  .  C  E  N  S  U  S
```

191

```
.  D  .  .  H  .  .  T  .
.  A  L  R  E  A  D  Y  .
.  N  E  A  R  .  A  R  C
.  C  A  G  E  .  T  E  A
H  E  R  S  .  .  E  .  B
.  .  N  .  R  I  S  E  S
.  S  E  W  E  D  .  Y  .
K  I  D  .  S  L  E  E  P
.  N  .  .  P  E  N  .  E
.  C  A  K  E  .  D  E  N
M  E  N  .  C  L  E  A  N
.  .  Y  E  T  .  D  R  Y
```

192

```
.  T  .  D  .  M  .  P  .
R  O  S  E  W  A  T  E  R
.  P  A  T  .  T  A  K  A
D  E  C  E  P  T  I  O  N
.  K  .  C  O  R  N  E  T
T  A  R  T  L  E  T  .  S
.  .  U  S  E  S  .  E  .
D  A  N  .  .  S  A  L  E
.  R  E  E  D  .  W  A  X
P  O  S  T  U  L  A  T  E
.  M  .  C  O  O  K  E  R
B  A  C  H  .  P  E  S  T
```

Solutions

193

	C			B				I
	R	E	S	O	L	V	E	D
	I	N	K	S		E		L
O	B	E	I	S	A	N	C	E
		M			R	U	H	R
	C	A	D	U	C	E	U	S
	H		I		A		T	
W	A	R	M	O	N	G	E	R
	R	U	N	N	E	R		E
	L	I	E	S		A	B	A
D	E	N	S	E		T	A	D
	S		S	T	R	E	S	S

194

	T			J		D		P
T	H	E	R	E		I	C	E
	E	X	O	T	I	C		N
L	E	T	S			T	E	N
		R	E	P	T	I	L	E
		E		A		O	D	D
M	E	M	B	R	A	N	E	
	N	E	E	D		A	R	T
	T		F	O	U	R		A
L	E	M	O	N		I	T	S
	R		R	E	P	E	A	T
A	S	K	E	D		S	P	Y

195

	B			F			B	
G	A	R	D	E	N	I	A	
	R	E	A	R		S	K	Y
	E	A	R	N		S	E	E
I	S	L	E			U		L
		I		G	E	E	U	P
	A	S	S	E	T		F	
D	O	E		S	N	O	O	P
	R			T	A	D		A
	T	A	T	A		O	U	T
B	A	D		P	A	U	S	E
		D	U	O		R	A	N

196

		D		P		L		U
T	I	A	R	A		O	L	D
		I		S	A	L	A	D
A	S	S	E	T		L	Y	E
	A		R	A	P	I	E	R
A	C	E	R		A	P	T	
		R		S	L	O	T	H
C	A	R	O	M		P	E	A
	S	A	L	O	N			S
L	I	T	I	G	I	O	U	S
	D	U	O		C	U	R	L
R	E	M		E	E	R	I	E

197

	A		C			R		
	G	R	A	P	P	A		C
B	O	E	R		I	N	F	O
		B	R	A	C	K	E	N
W	H	E	Y		K		E	
		L		W	E	L	S	H
	A	S	S	E	T	S		E
	B			S		D	I	M
R	E	C	I	T	E		N	
	D	O	V	E		B	A	T
		P	A	R	V	E	N	U
F	L	Y	N	N		D	E	N

198

	C			C			K	
	O	T	T	O	M	A	N	
	B	R	O	W		R	O	B
	R	A	I	L		M	B	A
F	A	I	L			E		L
		N		J	A	D	E	D
	K	E	B	A	B		L	
L	Y	E		C	L	I	M	B
	L			K	E	N		U
	I	O	W	A		L	S	D
H	E	R		S	T	A	I	D
		B	U	S		W	R	Y

Solutions

199

	V		A		P		B	
L	I	N	O		O	I	L	S
	S	E	R	V	E	S	U	P
	O	A	T		T	H	E	E
A	R	R	A	S		M		C
				Y	E	A	S	T
G	A	S		S	M	E	A	R
	P	A	S	T	I	L	L	E
	O	F	T	E	N		E	
	G	E	O	M	E	T	R	Y
	E	T	A		N	A	N	A
F	E	Y		S	T	R	O	P

200

	L			D		F		
C	O	R	D	O	B	A		V
	P			E	E	R	I	E
M	E	A	N	S	T	E	S	T
			L		S		I	
B	L	E	S	S		L	S	D
	L		T	O	M	E		A
C	A	D	E	T		G	U	M
	M		P		P		N	
O	A	F	S		R	E	I	N
		R	O	S	E	T	T	E
A	N	O	N		P	A	S	T

201

	I			G		B		E
K	O	R	E	A		E	L	L
	T	E	A	S	E	L		A
C	A	P	S			L	E	T
	R	E	C	E	I	V	E	
		O		O		G	A	D
R	E	V	E	L	L	E	D	
	M	E	L	D		R	E	B
	B		A	C	H	E		L
C	O	Y	P	U		N	E	O
	S		S	T	U	C	C	O
A	S	H	E	S		Y	U	M

202

		M		D		V		I
B	R	I	D	E		E	E	N
		L		L	A	R	V	A
C	H	E	S	T		T	E	N
	A		H	A	T	E		E
E	D	D	Y		A	B	A	
	E		G	O	R	S	E	
M	I	S	E	R		A	H	A
	S	T	O	O	P			S
S	L	I	N	G	S	H	O	T
	E	N	S		S	I	D	E
S	T	Y		U	T	T	E	R

203

			A			B		
C	A	P	S		O	N	E	S
	M	A	I	L	B	A	G	
	E	N	D		V	I	S	A
A	N	A	E	M	I	A		W
	M			O	D	I	N	
D	R	A	W		U		F	
	E		R	E	S	I	S	T
W	A	G	E	S		D		E
	S		A	P	P	E	A	R
P	O	U	T		H	A	R	M
	N		H	O	I	S	T	S

204

			O				H	
B	U	R	N		D	R	E	W
	F	A	C	T	U	A	L	
C	O	T	E		A	B	E	D
		I		B	L	I	N	I
O	B	O	E		E			C
	L		M	O	U	S	S	E
B	O	Y	S		S		I	
	N			C	E	L	E	B
	D	H	A	L		E	V	E
L	E	I		A	G	N	E	S
		M	E	W		D	D	T

Solutions

205

		I			M			
K	I	L	N		C	H	U	B
	R	A	C	C	O	O	N	
O	K	R	A		M	A	R	K
		V		B	A	R	O	N
C	I	A	O			S		O
	G		F	O	R	E	S	T
A	U	N	T		A		K	
	A			S	P	L	I	T
	N	O	D	E		A	N	A
J	A	W		C	H	I	N	K
		N	O	T		D	Y	E

206

		G		M		J		
T	R	E	A	S	U	R	E	D
	A	C	T		S		W	
	T	H	E	A	T	R	E	S
W	H	O		G		I	L	L
	E		C	O	L	D		I
E	R	G	O			G	O	D
		S	P	H	E	R	E	
H	A	I	T	I		A		
	C		U	N	W	I	N	D
T	R	A	M		Y	O	G	A
	E		E	V	E	N	E	D

207

	E		N			C		
	B	L	O	T	T	O		O
T	B	A	R		A	R	C	H
		S	T	A	R	D	O	M
S	A	S	H		T		C	
		I		J	A	C	O	B
	M	E	M	O	R	I	A	L
	A		B		T		A	
A	S	S	I	S	T	A	N	T
	H	O	D		I	D	E	A
		W	E	S	T	E	R	N
G	U	N	S		S	L	O	T

208

		P			F			
I	O	W	A		A	P	E	X
	P	A	Y	A	B	L	E	
	A	L	E		O	A	T	H
A	L	R	E	A	D	Y		A
		U		E	S	P	Y	
O	A	S	I	S			I	
	V		C	A	N	C	E	L
C	A	B	E	R		H		E
	T		C	I	C	A	D	A
D	A	T	A		H	O	O	F
	R		P	R	I	S	S	Y

209

	C		B		T		I	
T	A	P	E	W	O	R	M	
	R	U	T		P	U	P	A
	O	B	S	E	S	S		N
B	U	S		V		S	H	E
	S		S	E	R	I	A	L
H	E	M	A	N		A	L	E
	L		L		L		E	
		S	I	X	T	H		R
B	O	L	E		D	A	T	A
	D	I	N	E		R	I	P
K	E	P	T		P	E	N	T

210

	B		S			N		I
D	E	X	T	E	R	O	U	S
	L		O			U		L
A	L	L	O	W	A	N	C	E
	Y	O	D	E	L		R	
		S		N	E	X	U	S
O	D	E			C	E	D	E
	R		E			N	E	D
T	A	L	L	Y	H	O		A
	P	U	M	A		P	E	T
H	E	N		M	A	U	V	E
		G	A	S		S	A	D

Solutions

211

		H				D		
A	M	M	O		V	O	I	D
	A	I	R	L	I	N	E	
	G	N	U		K	I	T	E
S	E	I	S	M	I	C		A
	M			N	E	A	R	
D	I	S	C		G		C	
	N		A	S	S	E	T	S
C	U	T	U	P		X		E
	R		C	A	M	E	R	A
B	E	A	U		A	R	U	M
	D		S	P	O	T	T	Y

212

			T				D	
A	P	S	E		S	P	A	M
	O	P	E	N	A	I	R	
	U	R	N		L	A	T	H
F	R	I	S	I	A	N		A
	N			D	O	O	M	
S	A	G	A	S			I	
	N		S	T	I	F	L	E
C	O	P	S	E		L		X
	R		I	M	P	A	L	A
C	A	N	S		I	T	E	M
	K		T	H	E	S	I	S

213

	B		B			D		L
T	I	T	I	L	L	A	T	E
	K		P			M		F
D	E	T	E	R	R	E	N	T
	R	A	D	I	O		O	
		M		B	A	S	I	S
A	T	E			N	E	S	T
	H		G			T	E	A
R	E	M	A	I	N	S		T
	T	O	L	D		A	L	E
V	A	T		O	R	I	E	L
	E	E	L			L	A	Y

214

	B			S		J		
T	A	B	L	E	A	U		A
	K			A	L	T	A	R
R	E	C	U	M	B	E	N	T
		O			E		G	
S	T	O	P	P	R	E	S	S
	E		R	O	T	A	T	E
C	A	G	E	S		R		N
	T		S	E	A	L	E	D
D	I	C	E		L	O	P	E
	M		N	U	M	B	E	R
C	E	N	T		S	E	E	S

215

	B			B		C		
S	E	T	F	R	E	E		W
	A			A	D	D	L	E
S	T	O	N	E	D	E	A	D
	R				Y		S	
T	A	B	B	Y		A	S	P
	B		L	E	A	D		A
T	A	P	A	S		O	T	T
	T		N		E		I	
P	E	A	K		R	E	N	D
		L	E	G	A	T	E	E
B	E	L	T		S	C	A	N

216

	A		H					R
	M	A	H	A	R	A	J	A
	A	L	A	R		W		C
W	H	O	L	E	S	A	L	E
		H			T	R	I	M
	G	A	N	G	R	E	N	E
	A		O		O		E	
W	R	I	S	T	B	A	N	D
	A	N	T	H	E	M		R
	G	O	R	E		A	G	E
G	E	N	U	S		S	E	A
	S		M	E	S	S	E	D

Solutions

217

	T	F			B	V		
	A	L	L	T	H	E	R	E
	T	E	E			A	L	
A	T	T	E	M	P	T	E	D
		O	C	O	R	S	E	T
B	O	L	E	R	O		L	
		I		A	M	A	S	S
A	B	B	E	S		B		W
	R	E	A	S	S	U	M	E
B	I	R	R		A	S	I	A
	D	I	L	I	G	E	N	T
S	E	A	S		A	D	D	S

218

	F			F				R
	A	P	P	L	E	P	I	E
	C	L	U	E		H		V
S	T	A	L	E	M	A	T	E
		Z			U	S	E	R
	C	A	R	O	T	E	N	E
	R		E		A		O	
S	A	N	D	S	T	O	N	E
	C	A	R	T	E	R		V
	K	N	E	E		D	I	E
C	E	A	S	E		E	O	N
	D		S	P	U	R	N	S

219

		T				M		
A	Y	A	H		J	E	E	R
	E	M	I	N	E	N	T	
	T	O	R		A	N	E	W
B	I	R	D	F	L	U		A
	A				O	I	L	S
B	U	L	B		U		E	
	P		R	U	S	S	I	A
A	L	I	A	S		L		V
	O		C	A	N	A	P	E
F	A	R	E		U	S	E	R
	D		S	U	N	H	A	T

220

	G		S		B			F
	N	A	T	I	O	N	A	L
C	U	B	E		I			A
		S	W	A	L	L	O	W
C	R	U	S	T		O	W	L
		R		T	W	I	N	E
F	A	D		A		R		S
	D		B	R	I	E	F	S
W	A	V	E		M		L	
	G		S	E	P	S	I	S
T	I	N	E	A		A	C	T
	O		T	R	I	C	K	Y

221

			B		C		Z	
R	I	S	E		R	H	E	A
	F	A	R	R	I	E	R	
	F	L	Y		S	M	O	G
M	Y	A	L	G	I	A		A
	M				S	N	A	P
S	P	I	R	E			G	
	E		H	A	W	S	E	R
C	A	G	E	S		H		O
	K		S	T	R	A	I	T
M	E	N	U		A	F	R	O
	D		S	E	T	T	E	R

222

	I		Q		C		A	
	R	O	U	G	H	A	G	E
P	E	R	I		E		A	
		A	R	R	E	A	R	S
	G	N	E	I	S	S		P
		G		B	E	I	G	E
J	O	E	Y			D	E	W
	R		I		H	E	R	S
B	A	T	E	D			M	
	C	O	L		A	S	A	P
	L	A	D		T	U	N	A
L	E	D		A	M	B	E	R

Solutions

223

		G				T		
L	E	G	O		D	H	O	W
	A	I	R	S	H	I	P	
Q	U	A	Y		A	N	E	W
	N		U	L	T	R	A	
G	O	T	O			E		F
	P		A	M	I	D	S	T
L	I	S	T		C		E	
	A		B	E	T	E	L	
	T	O	F	U		H	O	E
S	E	N		C	H	A	F	E
		E	L	K		I	F	S

224

	G			B			T	
	N	I	N	E	V	E	H	
	A	N	O	N		V	A	T
	S	A	N	D		A	I	R
S	H	I	E	S		C		A
		D			B	U	O	Y
	C	O	L	L	E	E	N	
S	O	F	A		L	E	E	S
	A		C		L			E
	C	L	E	F		A	W	N
R	H	O		A	L	I	A	S
		B	I	D		D	Y	E

225

	G			S		P		L
C	O	M	P	E	T	E		I
	N			A	H	E	A	D
D	E	N	Y		A	L	S	O
		A			T		A	
A	B	Y	S	S		O	P	T
	L		W	A	R	N		A
B	A	S	E	D		E	M	U
	D		A		T		E	
P	E	A	T		O	S	L	O
		S	E	R	R	I	E	D
U	S	S	R		I	C	E	D

226

	M		F		B		H	
	O	R	A	T	O	R	I	O
	J	A	R		R		V	
C	O	M	M	A	N	D	E	R
		P		T	E	R	S	E
P	E	S	T	O		Y		S
	D			P	A	U	S	E
L	O	R	E		S	P	A	T
		A			H		I	
	U	N	I	C	Y	C	L	E
B	L	I	N	I		R	O	M
	T		S	A	T	Y	R	S

227

		R		O		S		
F	R	E	E	S	T	Y	L	E
	O	F	F		I		E	
	S	T	R	I	C	K	E	N
B	A	S	I	L		E	V	A
	R		G	L	I	D	E	R
B	Y	R	E		G		K	
		R	E	C	E	S	S	
S	A	H	A	R	A		C	
	D		T	A	R	T	A	R
L	E	G	O		T	I	L	E
	N		R	U	S	S	E	T

228

	J			A		C		S
M	I	X	U	P		A	F	T
	B			O	H	M		R
N	E	E	D	S		E	R	E
		D		T	H	R	E	E
R	A	G		L		A	C	T
	M	E	L	E	E		T	
	P		I			Y	O	D
T	E	R	R	A	C	E		E
	R	E	A	R		A	L	I
B	E	N		M	A	R	E	S
		T	O	Y		N	I	T

Solutions

229

	S		G		A		D	
C	O	L	L	E	C	T	E	D
	U		O	A	T		G	
C	R	O	S	S		M	R	S
	C		S	T	R	E	E	T
L	E	A			A	R	E	A
	C	L	O	V	E			B
S	T	R	I	K	E		G	
	E	T	A		T	U	G	
M	E	A	T	Y		S	A	N
	A	G	E		N	A	N	A
S	T	E	R	N		R	O	W

230

	T			P		A		D
	H	O	M	E		T	A	R
	E	V	E	N	S	O		O
D	E	E	R			M	A	W
		R	E	M	A	I	N	S
		D		U		C	O	Y
S	C	U	R	R	I	E	D	
	R	E	E	D		N	E	T
	E		G	E	N	E		I
F	A	K	I	R		R	O	M
	S		M	E	A	G	R	E
N	E	W	E	R		Y	E	S

231

		C		A		A		
M	A	L	I	C	I	O	U	S
	W	I	T		D		G	
	H	A	Y	F	E	V	E	R
A	I	R		O		I	R	A
	L		A	P	E	S		R
F	E	E	S			I	C	E
			C	U	T	T	E	R
A	S	H	E	S			R	
	K		T	A	B	L	E	T
H	I	F	I		U	T	A	H
	D		C	U	D	D	L	E

232

	S		E			B		D
	A	B	U	D	H	A	B	I
	L	A	C			S		C
F	I	S	H	S	L	I	C	E
	N		R	H	E	S	U	S
G	E	N	E	R	A		B	
		I		I	N	S	E	T
E	G	G	O	N		K		I
	R	E	C	K	L	E	S	S
B	A	L	E		O	W	L	S
	F	L	A	M	B	E	A	U
S	T	A	N		E	D	G	E

233

	R			S			D	
C	A	F	F	E	I	N	E	
	T	R	O	T		A	R	C
S	T	A	S	H		I	V	Y
	L	I	T			R		S
	E	L	E	P	H	A	N	T
	S	T	R	A	Y		O	
A	N	Y		S	M	A	R	T
	A			T	N	T		R
	K	I	W	I		L	O	U
B	E	T		M	E	A	N	S
	S	U	E		S	O	T	

234

	A		C		H		C	
E	S	C	A	L	A	T	O	R
	S	A	L		L	E	V	I
P	U	R	L	O	I	N	E	D
	M	B	A		B	E	R	G
L	E	U		O	U	T		E
		R	A	F	T		P	
S	M	E	L	T		N	O	W
	A	T	E		P	A	R	A
E	N	T	R	Y		C	O	G
	G	O	T	O		R	U	E
H	E	R		D	R	E	S	S

235

	C			C			B	
P	O	R	P	O	I	S	E	
	B	E	E	R		L	E	T
	R	E	A	D		A	P	E
B	A	N	K			B		L
		T		N	A	S	A	L
	B	R	I	E	F		D	
R	O	Y		S	A	N	D	Y
	O			T	R	Y		O
	T	Y	P	E		L	E	K
A	H	A		G	L	O	V	E
		M	U	G		N	E	D

236

			B				F	
F	E	T	E		P	L	A	N
	C	A	R	T	O	O	N	
	R	U	E		S	I	G	N
F	U	R	T	H	E	R		I
		U			S	E	L	L
M	U	S	E	S			E	
	N		R	A	I	S	E	D
S	C	R	A	G		L		E
	O		S	A	H	A	R	A
J	I	V	E		U	P	O	N
	L		S	E	N	S	E	S

237

	S		B		C		C	
	T	E	A	R	A	W	A	Y
	U	R	N		D		R	
U	N	A	S	H	A	M	E	D
		T		E	V	A	D	E
	L	O	O	M	E	D		M
	O			P	R	A	D	O
B	O	L	D		O	M	E	N
		I			U		S	
F	A	N	T	A	S	T	I	C
	G	E	A	R		U	R	I
	E	D	G	E		B	E	D

238

	E			E		S		D
	S	I	L	L		I	K	E
	A	N	I	M	U	S		M
R	U	F	F			T	W	A
		L	E	C	T	E	R	N
		A		O		R	I	D
S	A	M	E	N	E	S	S	
	R	E	N	T		I	T	S
	M		G	R	I	N		E
M	A	C	A	O		L	A	N
	D		G	L	O	A	T	S
C	A	K	E	S		W	E	E

239

	M			W		W		H
F	O	R	T	H		A	G	A
	J	O	Y	O	U	S		M
R	O	O	K			H	A	S
		S	E	R	V	A	N	T
		T		I		B	Y	E
F	O	E	H	N		L		R
	B	R	U	S	S	E	L	S
	L		L	E	O		E	
B	A	A	L		G	R	A	B
	T	I	S		G	U	R	U
E	E	L		H	Y	M	N	S

240

			I		F		J	
F	E	R	O	C	I	O	U	S
	N	E	W		R		D	
	D	I	A	B	E	T	E	S
S	E	N		O		R	A	T
	A		M	A	N	Y		A
E	R	G	O			S	R	I
			N	E	C	T	A	R
M	I	N	O	R			D	
	M		C	A	T	N	I	P
B	A	I	L		H	O	U	R
	M		E	V	E	N	S	O

Solutions

241

	P			O			F	
	A	S	T	R	I	D	E	
	S	C	A	B		R	U	B
	T	A	N	S		O	D	E
B	A	N	K			P		V
	D		N	A	S	T	Y	
	B	A	B	E	S		E	
P	A	L		W	I	V	E	S
	S			N	A	Y		H
	T	A	K	E		I	D	O
Z	E	N		S	E	N	N	A
		Y	E	S		G	A	L

242

		A	F		L	
P	R	A	G	M	A	T	I	C
	E	R	R		D		V	
	D	I	A	B	E	T	E	S
B	U	D		O		A	S	H
	C		V	A	M	P		I
G	E	N	E			E	A	R
			T	H	I	R	S	T
A	D	I	E	U			S	
	I		R	E	T	A	I	N
G	A	L	A		U	R	S	A
	Z		N	A	P	K	I	N

243

	E		B			I		
	T	A	I	L	O	R		C
B	A	N	D		B	I	R	O
		G	E	N	E	S	I	S
S	I	L	T		Y		L	
		E		C	E	L	L	O
	A	R	C	A	D	E		D
	I			T		D	U	D
U	L	S	T	E	R		P	
	S	T	I	R		B	E	G
		A	N	E	M	O	N	E
A	N	G	E	R		O	D	E

244

			K			J	
G	C	S	E		A	G	O	G
	Y	A	N	K	I	N	G	
	S	T	Y		D	A	S	H
S	T	E	A	M	E	R		A
		E			S	L	A	M
R	I	N	G	S			I	
	G		R	E	A	L	M	S
P	U	R	E	E		E		O
	A		E	R	R	A	T	A
I	N	O	N		A	S	A	P
	A		S	A	F	E	T	Y

245

	C			B			A	
	I	M	P	O	R	T	S	
	G	A	I	N		A	I	D
	A	X	L	E		D	A	Y
C	R	I	E	S		P		E
		M			C	O	L	D
	B	U	F	F	A	L	O	
C	A	M	E		S	E	T	S
	D		A		T			W
	G	E	R	M		B	E	E
P	E	A		A	W	A	R	E
		T	O	Y		G	A	P

246

	E		B			L		A
R	A	P	I	D	F	I	R	E
	V		P			R		R
N	E	C	E	S	S	A	R	Y
	S	I	D	L	E		E	
		T		Y	A	C	H	T
B	E	E			T	H	A	W
	L		D			A	B	E
N	O	S	E	B	A	G		L
	P	A	N	E		R	A	F
B	E	T		S	H	I	F	T
		E	F	T		N	T	H

Solutions

247

	B			E		H		
	A	B	L	E		E	N	D
	B	E	A	K	E	R		O
O	A	R	S			E	E	L
		S	T	U	B	B	L	E
		E		G		Y	E	S
M	A	R	S	H	Y		M	
	E	K	E			P	I	P
	G		C	A	F	E		A
N	E	V	E	R		R	A	Y
	A		D	I	V	I	N	E
U	N	W	E	D		L	Y	E

248

			E				G	
C	O	R	D		F	I	A	T
	R	A	I	L	I	N	G	
	A	B	C		L	U	S	T
S	L	I	T	H	E	R		A
		E		S	E	A	T	
L	A	S	E	R		X		
	V		S	O	R	B	E	T
F	O	N	T	S		L		E
	C		A	E	R	A	T	E
B	E	A	T		O	D	I	N
	T		E	X	C	E	S	S

249

	C			P		K		
C	O	R	D	I	T	E		I
	M			C	O	P	R	A
D	A	L	M	A	T	I	A	N
		E			T		V	
F	L	A	T	T	E	R	E	R
	E		S	E	R	E	N	E
B	A	T	H	E		T		S
	K		I	N	S	I	S	T
F	A	I	R		A	N	T	I
	G		T	Y	C	O	O	N
W	E	T	S		S	L	A	G

250

	B			B		A		
F	A	R	R	I	E	R		B
	B			L	A	T	T	E
D	E	P	R	E	S	S	E	D
		A			Y		E	
A	S	T	I	R		A	S	S
	H		C	O	N	S		A
B	A	S	E	D		H	O	G
	P		D		R		F	
M	E	E	T		O	P	T	S
		L	E	G	A	T	E	E
S	O	Y	A		R	A	N	T

251

	T		R		L		L	
M	E	M	O	R	I	S	E	
	R	E	D		F	I	T	S
	M	E	S	S	E	S		C
H	I	T		E		T	A	R
	N		S	E	V	E	R	E
C	A	R	T	S		R	A	W
	L		R		Y		B	
		T	O	N	E	S		B
C	O	R	K		T	O	R	E
	W	E	E	P		L	I	E
B	L	E	D		G	O	D	S

252

	E		D		F		C	
	C	H	A	I	R	M	A	N
	H	U	T		U		P	
S	O	M	E	T	I	M	E	S
		A		S	T	A	S	H
N	I	N	J	A		C		U
	M			R	O	A	S	T
A	P	E	X		R	O	W	S
		X			C		E	
	M	A	S	S	A	C	R	E
C	A	M	E	O		A	V	E
	D		E	N	A	M	E	L

Solutions

253

	C			G			D	
	O	V	E	R	A	W	E	
	M	A	L	E		H	E	N
	M	U	S	E		I	D	O
V	A	L	E	T		M		I
		T			S	P	U	R
	T	E	R	R	I	E	R	
B	O	D	E		C	R	I	B
	R		N		K			U
	S	H	O	P		M	P	G
B	O	O		E	M	A	I	L
		P	U	G		T	E	E

254

			H		C		G	
S	E	V	E	R	A	L	L	Y
	N	I	L		D		U	
	S	E	M	E	S	T	E	R
B	U	D		V		U	S	A
	R		P	E	A	L		B
Z	E	T	A			L	E	A
			R	E	C	E	N	T
S	L	E	E	K			G	
	A		S	E	P	S	I	S
A	N	T	I		H	O	N	K
	D		S	Y	D	N	E	Y

255

	C			L			M	
W	A	R	H	O	R	S	E	
	S	O	O	T		A	G	A
	T	O	S	S		L	A	X
J	E	S	T			E		I
		T		A	S	S	E	S
	B	E	V	E	L		C	
B	A	R		R	E	B	U	S
	D			O	W	L		P
	G	E	E	S		A	K	A
G	E	M		O	A	S	E	S
		S	A	L		T	A	M

256

			I			B		
L	I	O	N		S	L	O	P
	D	O	G	S	T	A	R	
	E	D	O		A	R	E	S
H	A	L	T	I	N	G		I
		E			D	O	O	R
T	A	S	E	R		B		
	M		M	E	M	O	I	R
R	A	B	I	D		C		A
	Z		G	O	T	H	I	C
B	E	A	R		E	R	N	E
	D		E	X	C	E	S	S

257

	E		G		T		J	
	D	A	R	K	R	O	O	M
L	O	B	E		A		K	
		B	E	M	U	S	E	D
	P	A	N	A	M	A		R
		C		P	A	L	S	Y
S	T	Y	E		V	I	A	
	H		L		B	E	N	D
L	I	M	I	T		C		
	R	I	O		A	G	E	S
	T	N	T		R	A	R	E
D	Y	E		S	C	R	E	W